SELF-HEALING ANXIETY

A Practical Guide For Women. A Heart-Centered Guide To Stop Overthinking The Past And Worrying About The Future

DR. SAMANTHA WELLAPPILI

Life and Soul
Medicine

Contents

Part II
Embracing Wholeness

© Copyright 2023 - All rights reserved.

The content contained within this book may not be reproduced, duplicated, or transmitted without direct written permission from the author or the publisher.

Under no circumstances will any blame or legal responsibility be held against the publisher, or author, for any damages, reparation, or monetary loss due to the information contained within this book, either directly or indirectly.

Legal Notice:

This book is copyright protected. It is only for personal use. You cannot amend, distribute, sell, use, quote or paraphrase any part, or the content within this book, without the consent of the author or publisher.

Disclaimer Notice:

Please note the information contained within this document is for educational and entertainment purposes only. All effort has been executed to present accurate, up to date, reliable, complete information. No warranties of any kind are declared or implied. Readers acknowledge that the author is not engaged in the rendering of legal, financial, medical or professional advice. The content within this book has been derived from various sources. Please consult a licensed professional before attempting any techniques outlined in this book.

By reading this document, the reader agrees that under no circumstances is the author responsible for any losses, direct or indirect, that are incurred as a result of the use of the information contained within this document, including, but not limited to, errors, omissions, or inaccuracies.

All patient histories shared in this book have been anonymized and are included with consent.

Introduction

The Soul always knows what to do to heal itself. The challenge is to silence the mind.

Caroline Myss

Women: Mental Health Facts

Joanne was elegantly dressed, with a designer leather bag and glossy hair. At first glance, she was a successful businesswoman, but at closer inspection, she was pale, dizzy, had constant headaches, and complained about fatigue. Dr. Wellappili asked her a few questions. Joanne's voice was low, as if she was too exhausted to speak. Yes, her heart often started racing without any reason. Yes, she experienced night sweats. Yes, she felt weak and often nauseous.

Screening tests confirmed my suspicions: anxiety, probably combined with a lack of sleep. A little voice told me to look a bit deeper. Too many Joannes came to see me. They sat across my desk: exhausted, confused, embarrassed, unable to meet the expectations placed on them, and sometimes even angry. A constant flow of women came to me for help with chronic fatigue, persistent colds, nagging nonspecific stomach issues, exhaustion, and insomnia. Most of these conditions were treatable, but the women returned exhausted and irritable despite treatment.

My name is Dr. Samantha Wellappili, and I am a British medical practitioner who worked as a family doctor in London for many years. As the number of distraught, anxious, and exhausted women grew, I sensed my patients' emotional turmoil might be a prime cause of their ailing physical health. I had a thriving career and a secure future in the conventional medical world. My practice was busy, and there was barely time to do more than treat these women for their physical health conditions.

Despite time constraints, I could not ignore the hidden emotional pain that so often manifested in ill health. An alarming number of my female patients struggled mentally. The information in my patient files confirmed my suspicions: At least one in five women suffered from a common mental health problem, often accompanied by anxiety.

My carefully-phrased questions revealed an alarming picture: About three-quarters of these women indicated they had experienced mental health problems since their late teens or early twenties.

Most patients, like Joanne, seemed fine on the surface. They had learned to mask their emotions with a layer of efficiency and determination to be successful. Consequently, few had the insight to seek professional help for their emotional problems. In most cases, their family, friends, and colleagues were unaware of their deep-seated mental struggles. The Joannes of the world bit the bullet and got on with their lives, often juggling impressive careers, motherhood, and marriage, but ended up physically sick at their doctors' offices.

Many patients mentioned stress and toxic relationships at work. Others had a troubled family life. The women across my desk sought help for physical problems, but also needed emotional care and practical guidance for untangling problems elsewhere.

I treated their physical symptoms, but knew prescription medicines alone could not heal their high anxiety levels. I increasingly realized conventional medication alone does not always resolve recurring negative patterns in life, or support healthy relationships.

The realization that I could not treat people's emotional needs with conventional medicine forced me to take stock of my own life. And, after a life-changing experience of burnout and feeling disillusioned with a purely disease-focused role, I left my office and hung up my white coat to switch my focus to radiant health instead. Like so many of my patients, I needed to take some time to rethink my life and priorities. I never wanted to withdraw from life. I wanted to live a full and meaningful life without mental exhaustion, papering over the cracks instead of confronting the root cause of the problem.

My health and wellness journey took me across Asia and the United States of America. Enriched by my studies and travels, I returned to London and founded Life and Soul Medicine. For the past 15 years, I have worked with individuals, leading health specialists, and corporate groups, helping clients adopt a balanced lifestyle, find access to their inner joy, and integrate this into their busy lives. Working on health and well-being from the inside out through daily choices and habits prevents the early onset of lifestyle diseases and accelerates recovery when ill or injured. On top of that, medical costs, and recovery time are significantly reduced, bringing financial relief to employers and the individual.

I do not claim to have a magic wand. As a medical doctor with years of experience, I believe in the effectiveness of conventional medical and psychological treatment. I fully support prescription drugs for medical conditions, and appreciate the value of counseling services.

However, I strongly recommend a holistic approach to balance mental, emotional, and spiritual well-being as the key to enduring physical health. We are not machines; we need sleep and self-care. This book's practices can radically improve mental health, with or without conventional treatment. I spent years on research, and the result is a body of specially-designed techniques, practices, and exercises that address anxiety.

Media reports stoked more anxiety, worry, and fear during the pandemic than ever before. Often, conflicting expert opinions further aggravated the anxiety. With this social state as the backdrop, many are trying to get back to normal, but we ask ourselves: What is normal?

Typical of the instant gratification culture of the 21st century, many of my patients wanted quick fixes with minimum effort. Many women stated outright that they did not have the time or inclination for years of therapy and soul-seeking about past traumas. Others expressed the wish to lessen their intake of prescription drugs.

The practices in this book are designed to support you in recognizing and shifting behavior patterns, such as endlessly dwelling on the past, or enduring crippling worries about the future. The effects of these shifts are visible after only a few weeks, and often have a surprising effect on general health. Many women experiencing daily anxiety have found their spark again using the techniques outlined in these pages. Also, my clients have found that the self-healing journey has a ripple effect, improving their mental, emotional, and physical health, family dynamics, and professional lives. Their lives reflected a newly-discovered inner strength and trust in themselves.

If you are at an emotional low point in your life, take medicine for chronic disease, and still feel as if you are about to spin out of control, this is the book for you. Explore a new approach to your life right there where you are. Nobody can wave a magic wand to delete your past or your pain. Nonetheless, centuries of collected wisdom combined with cutting-edge medical and psychological research will give you the tools to find your spark again.

Burnout, anxiety, and disillusionment hit me hard at a critical point in my life. Not even my profession, experience, or knowledge could protect me from life's curveballs. I was fortunate to be able to take extended time off to rest and rejuvenate. I found another way to live my life away from toxic influences and to dedicate attention and focus to how I wanted to serve moving forward. How could I use all my medical knowledge and incorporate as much ancient wisdom as possible to bring a whole new level to my contribution?

I am grateful for this because many women must keep going despite their inner turmoil. Even if you can't pack your bags and leave, you can rid yourself of your emotional baggage through the practices explained in the following chapters.

This low point in my life eventually led me to further research and opened the door to an exciting new field in my medical career: holistic health, blending care for the mind, body, heart, and Soul. This book is my way of sharing the grace I received during that dark phase with you.

A Note on "Negative" Thoughts and Behaviors

Throughout this book, negative thoughts and behaviors are referred to. This is for brevity; a better way to describe these would be thoughts and behaviors that no longer serve. This acknowledges that in general, patterns that we now view as negative, were created to protect us at an earlier stage.

Let's look at the example of Liz, the perfectionist. When Liz was a child, she learned that to get the attention, praise, and affection she desired, she needed high grades at school and to be captain of the hockey team. This attention, praise, and affection made her feel safe and loved. She continued this learned pattern of perfectionism into adulthood, and it brought stress, anxiety, and exhaustion, so we can see that it no longer serves her and this formerly helpful pattern has become a "negative" behavior pattern, causing her distress.

PART I

Prioritizing Health and Happiness

The Mind and the Body

Start now. Start where you are. Start with fear. Start with pain. Start with doubt. Start with hands shaking. Start with voice trembling but start. Start and don't stop. Start where you are, with what you have. Just…Start.

Pema Chödrön

Does This Sound Too Close for Comfort?

YOU ARE CONSTANTLY ill with coughs, colds, or stomach upsets, feeling tired all the time and your medical insurance is usually depleted by mid-year. You are persistently worried about your health, your husband's fidelity, your finances, and your boss' mood. A dog's incessant barking, your colleague's long lunches, and your friend's insincere smile are irritating. Every time your children are late home from school, you expect an emergency call from the hospital. Often, you feel bone tired but can't sleep without a sleeping pill. You fixate on your looks, and whether your weight, height, or complexion is as good as your sister's or friend's. Perhaps you avoid socializing, as you fear people will snub you because you are not as well-dressed or well-informed. You can't let go of the injustices of the past, and relive those hurtful or humiliating moments over and over. You are sometimes angry and sometimes sad, but find a few glasses to fill the void.

If any of the above seem to fit your private thoughts, it is time to check in with yourself. You don't need to live by the narrative that you're a victim of circumstance. There is a way to avoid being another of these statistics:

- In the United States, more women (one in five) than men (one in eight) suffer from mental health disorders.
- Abused women are more likely to suffer from mental health disorders.
- Poverty contributes to women developing mental health issues.
- Women of all ethnic groups suffer from mental health problems, with higher percentages among Asian, Black, and minority groups.
- Three-quarters of women with mental health problems have had these issues since their early twenties.
- Women are more likely to attempt or commit suicide than men.
- Girls contacting Childline mentioned suicidal thoughts regularly. (Women's Mental Health Facts, n.d.).

This does not have to be you. You can have a full and meaningful life as you learn to take care of and prioritize your mental, emotional, and spiritual health. If you are exhausted, overworked, a struggling parent, or have a history of trauma, healing will only start with a conscious, brave, decision to help yourself. The techniques described in this book are designed to be easily integrated into your daily life, bit by bit, tweak by tweak. The content of this book is founded on sound medical knowledge, extensive postgraduate research, and years of experience in holistic care and lifestyle medicine. The techniques in this book are easily accessible and can be simply integrated into your daily life.

While this book imparts wisdom and shares an opportunity to change your life, the real challenge lies in your commitment to yourself. Take the first step and check in with yourself as you go. Note the small positive changes, and find a way to celebrate these. Change up your self-talk; you can do this step by step. They might seem insignificant, but every inch forward will be motivation to keep going. Give your mind and body a few weeks to adapt, and you will be surprised.

Take note at this stage that your anxiety did not develop overnight. Changing negative thought patterns and established emotional loops will take time, effort, great kindness to yourself, acceptance of your humanness, and the grit to keep going. Do not give up, and do not feel guilty; no journey of transformation is a straight line upward. We all make mistakes, but our mistakes and traumas should not determine the rest of our lives.

Nelson Mandela said: "Do not judge me by my successes; judge me by how many times I fell down and got back up again."

Holistic health care focuses on the whole person; therefore, the mind and body deserve the same care and attention to achieve optimal mental, emotional, and physical robustness. Many of us are used to seeking help for physical problems but will shy away from seeking help with mental or emotional distress, deeming this as somehow unimportant.

This chapter will help you understand how the mind and body influence each other. It explains how and why your mental and emotional state affects your body and can make you sick.

Brain, Mind, and Body Connection

What has Spirituality Got to Do with My Anxiety and Stress?

Spirituality is a much-discussed term and holds different meanings for many of us. For religious people, it could mean following a specific set of beliefs according to a fixed values system bringing faith, comfort and community. Others see spirituality in another context, as knowing you are part of something bigger than yourself, feeling deeply connected to nature and those around you, and this intuitive knowing and connection fuels purpose.

Medical experts and researchers increasingly believe that a collaborative, holistic approach to patients' health and well-being leads to improved health outcomes and reduced frequency of chronic illness. Experts agree that spirituality is essential to the holistic mental and physical healing approach. But how does it work?

We all know that we feel better when listening to beautiful music or an inspiring speaker. But the beauty of the moment and the positive emotion pass quickly, and you are back to square one: sad and anxious. Mindful spiritual practices, those that we give our full attention, are calming, provide meaning, and stimulate the brain to release feel-good hormones. Over time, with regular practice, the prefrontal region of the brain changes, improving your ability to self-regulate your responses and impulsivity, to plan ahead and to balance your emotions. These changes act as a protective layer against anxiety and stress triggered by external factors.

Recent advances in neuroscience show that even in adulthood, the brain itself can physically change and develop new pathways through neuroplasticity—we can grow and develop the brain throughout our lives. Even adult brains can create new pathways, which open the possibility of new thought patterns. One way of doing this is through repeated and sustained spiritual practices.

This is a message of hope and joy to every woman who suffers from mental health issues. You can choose to develop a new perspective on life with positive behaviors that reinforce healing and beneficial messages to your brain. A religious person might repeat a phrase from the Bible or the Quran, and a Buddhist might use a favorite chant. Non-religious people often repeat inspiring quotes or simple words of gratitude. Whatever speaks to you can help you reprogram negative patterns in your brain's inner workings and create physical changes in the brain.

Spiritual practices, furthermore, help individuals develop better coping mechanisms. People often practice their preferred spirituality with a like-minded group, and the group's support can be precious. Later in this book, you will learn about non-religious spiritual practices such as mindfulness, meditation, exercise, and breathing techniques; also, several traditional Eastern methods will surprise you with their simplicity and effectiveness. And the beauty is that none of these need to oppose or question your religious or cultural traditions; on the contrary, they will complement and enhance any existing spiritual practices.

The Brain and the Mind: What's the Difference?

You know where your brain is, but where is your mind located? What is the mind? Are the brain and the mind the same?

Neuroscientists tell us the brain and the mind are not the same. However, they are interconnected and inseparable. Think of the mind as energy and the brain as an organic machine using the energy to change, grow, and evolve. The brain uses the mind to formulate ideas, thoughts, facts, and feelings. It can't function without the mind, but the mind is so powerful that it can change the brain.

When we talk about the mind, we're using the term to describe aspects of what goes on inside our brain. People often use the two terms interchangeably, but they're not the same.

There are different physical elements to your brain, which you can easily see in any diagram, but your mind is what goes on within that physical organ.

Since the middle of the 20th century, neuroscientists have used the computer as an analogy to explain the interaction between the brain and the mind. Although an oversimplification to which many scientists object (Knapp, 2012), the analogy helps us understand the complexity of the brain and the mind. Think of the brain as your computer's hardware, and the mind as the software.

Essentially, your brain contains nerve cells (called neurons) connected through synapses. These cells transport messages through the brain and nervous system.

These neural networks, or pathways, can be strengthened through repetition of behaviors and thought patterns. This is how we form habits and patterns—either beneficial ones, or ones that can harm us. Likewise, these pathways can be consciously and unconsciously influenced and supported by what we do, the influences we have in our lives, and past experiences, beliefs, and values we have stored in our minds.

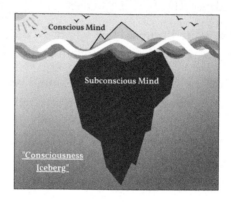

Your subconscious mind is thought to be responsible for over 95% of your behavior day to day, and your early childhood experiences largely programmed it up until the age of seven (Lipton, 2005). Imagine, each of us, throughout adulthood, is being heavily influenced by our inner seven-year-old's world view!

The mind works consciously and subconsciously. While we sleep, the mind continues its work on a subconscious level. Have you ever woken up and remembered a forgotten name, or the details of something you could not pinpoint the previous day? Your subconscious mind was busy while you rested and found the answer stored in your memory bank.

The brain is our incredible mental processing and storage organ. Through a complex system of chemical neurotransmitters, electrical impulses, nerves, and hormones, it informs our mental and emotional states and communicates with the rest of the physical body.

How to Use Cutting-Edge Science to Improve Mental Health

Researchers have strong evidence that the brain can change when we "change our minds." You may ask yourself: *How does this help me clear my anxiety, overthinking, and burnout?*

Remember, your mind (conscious and subconscious) controls the brain's responses; thus, you can use your mind in a specific way to generate positive changes. It is not easy to change your mind, especially if you have been in a negative mindset for an extended period. You need time to internalize your decision and adapt your behavior to bring about changes. It takes a while for new thought and behavior patterns to be created and set into brain and body cells.

Easier said than done, you might rightly say. You have been along that way quite often. You know sugar is terrible for you, but you still buy cheesecake instead of a fruit salad at lunchtime. You know your teenager has bedtime rules, but ignore her late-night phone use to avoid confrontation. We tend to know what is right, but we often do the opposite.

How can the information in this book help you change your mind and brain structure to reroute negative thoughts and emotions to live more positively?

The answer is to start with your body. The body influences your state of mind. A physically relaxed body sends calming messages to the brain. Negative thoughts and behavior patterns created in the mind are released, bringing peace to the system. Thus, your body plays a significant and often overlooked part in your mental health.

The Mind-Body Connection

Stress does not only overwhelm your mind. Your body picks up on tension in a heartbeat. The term fight-or-flight describes how the body readies itself for danger. Centuries ago, our ancestors managed to survive because their bodies went into emergency mode when threatened. The same applies to the 21st century. We use our bodies' miraculous ability to go into overdrive to protect ourselves and our loved ones.

As soon as the mind senses danger, it notifies the brain. As soon as you sense danger, the pituitary gland in the brain releases stress hormones that rush to the adrenal glands. Cortisol and adrenaline step in and prepare the body for action. Your breathing becomes quicker and your heart races, sending more oxygen to your muscles. As with most things, a little can be helpful, and too much can be harmful. Let's look at what happens physically in the body:

- Stress increases the heart rate to accelerate the delivery of fresh blood to muscles and limbs, but long-term increases combined with high blood pressure weaken the arteries and may lead to heart disease and even stroke.
- Prolonged stress interferes with the reproductive system and can lead to missed periods, infertility, and low sex drive.
- Stress contributes to insomnia, a weakened immune system, dysregulated blood sugar, and the development of type 2 diabetes.
- Stress prepares muscles for life-saving action, but persistent stress can lead to tension, muscle pain, and back pain.
- Stress affects the digestive system and contributes to nausea, indigestion, diarrhea, constipation, and associated illnesses.

How Can You Build Your Resilience to Stress?

All the advice in the world will not help if you don't take responsibility for your role in creating health and harmony in your incredible body, mind, heart, and Soul. The very first step is to recognize and feel your emotions instead of stuffing them down like they are not important. Your emotions are valid and deserve your acknowledgment by feeling them, naming them, and being honest with yourself about their origins.

Don't underestimate the value of this seemingly small step. Allowing emotion to naturally move through us by feeling it stops it from "sticking." It is felt in fullness and then passes, a short process of a few minutes. If we hold on to it and push it down, when we weave stories and reasons all around it, it lodges in our system and can stick around for years. By recognizing and naming an emotion, we create space. We are then able to feel that emotion instead of avoiding it. Think of that emotion as energy; energy in motion = e-motion. By feeling that e-motion we have named, it is acknowledged, and it's allowed to move through us instead of being ignored or suppressed, only to pop up later down the line.

You might recognize the sensation of passive aggression when you feel anger for a transgression. It seeps out over time in normal daily interactions, and the actual issue is not addressed. Passive aggression can really poison a relationship.

Another common pattern used to avoid feeling difficult emotions is stuffing down a difficult emotion following an incident, then later getting overly angry or upset by something small, usually involving people unrelated to the original incident. It happens because cooped-up emotions are trying to move through you and be recognized and released, but this damaging pattern can sabotage healthy relationships.

Life can be overwhelming, but if you find yourself dwelling on negative thoughts or difficult experiences, the whys, what-ifs, and if onlys, recognize the pattern! Flip the script: Name and feel the dominant emotion. Allow it to flow through you. Can you feel it somewhere in your body? Can you move that part, massage that part, and care for that part of you? This is an advanced embodiment technique, and I've seen it bring calm to many who struggle to find peace in their emotions. The emotional, mental, and physical levels of our being are so intertwined, and the practices in this book will help you balance their interaction.

Chronic Illness and Mental Health

People with chronic health conditions are also more prone to developing mental health issues. In chronic disease states, there is a high level of background inflammation in the body. It is partly due to the elevated levels of stress hormones. A complex cascade of hormones and chemical messengers in the body impairs your immune system and how your body fights infection. Inflammation also contributes to weight gain around your middle and high blood pressure, poor digestion, headaches, acne, and hormonal imbalance.

I've listed some conditions that often have significant emotional components, whether anxiety or low mood. If any of these conditions concern you, it's a strong signal to check in with your emotional self regularly and take stock, to find your way back to inner balance and, ultimately, support your physical health.

- Cardiovascular disease
- Diabetes
- Autoimmune conditions
- Acne
- Chronic fatigue
- Obesity
- Addictions
- Menopause

Contact your doctor if you have concerns about your mental health. Also, discuss the advice in this guide with your doctor and get their support with any big changes you might want to make. You can move toward more balance and well-being, step by step, by putting one foot in front of the other.

Quick Reminder

- Doctors recognize the benefit of lifestyle changes that support mental, emotional, and spiritual balance to manage existing medical conditions and prevent the development of chronic disease.
- Nurturing your spirituality brings a sense of greater purpose, the ability to trust in yourself, and lessens anxiety.
- Consider the mind as the coalescence of your mental energy: your personality, ideas, habits, thoughts, worries, memories, and preferences.
- Long-term stress is tough on multiple body systems— digestive, immune, cardiovascular and hormonal—because of the increased background level of inflammation in the system.
- Start with your body, feel your emotions, and recognize if you can physically notice sensations in your body that accompany them.

The Energy Body and Your Health

In this chapter, I want to guide you into an unseen but very real part of the human experience: your energy body, the biofield, this unseen dimension of you that is so integral to your physical, emotional, and mental health. Think about it; you don't see your emotions, but you experience them daily. Similarly, these spiritual energy centers determine the balance of your energy body, a field of information exchange between your system and your environment that defines you emotionally, mentally, and physically from moment to moment.

Think of the seven chakras in your body as an energetic skeleton through which your mental, emotional, and energetic dimensions interact and influence your physical body.

What Are Chakras?

Chakras are the body's energy centers. The seven chakras of the body are commonly thought of as levels of consciousness; they work together to support your emotional, mental, and physical balance, and your energy field joins and interacts with the energy fields of those around you, exchanging information. Ancient cultures have known about this energy field for millennia. Modern science is increasingly interested in and recognizes the biofield as a legitimate study area.

All matter is energy. Everything you see and everything you don't see all around you is energy. People have written about the chakras for centuries—many of the qualities of chakras and their connections to the physical body overlap. The chakras are described in detail in ancient Indian and Buddhist texts. These sacred books extol the chakras' importance for human health. Today, yoga is commonplace all over the world; in fact, this is an ancient system designed to harmonize the chakras of the energy body, which might explain why this esoteric practice is highly regarded for bringing relaxation and vitality to the body.

During the 20th century, several Western spiritualists explored the role of chakras in healing and health and added to our knowledge of these energy sources. Writings of the 20th century connect chakras to colors, metals, crystals, minerals, astrological bodies, and tarot cards. Not all schools of thought agree on everything; nonetheless, there is a growing global trend looking to the energy body for deep healing.

On this journey to combat anxiety, we focus on seven chakras, or energy centers. These seven energy centers are located along the midline of the body. Like electricity, Wi-Fi, and radio waves, they are not visible, but these centers play a vital role in keeping you going.

Let's look at the seven chakras and their connections to body and mind. This foundational information will give a feel for your energy body as you get to know this new level of your body's magnificence and will guide you on how to work with these energy centers fully. Take note of the chakras, because blockages interrupt the smooth flow of energy around your system, and, if left unchecked, can lead to significant health issues. Below is a short description of each chakra, its English name, location in your body, and its function or 'responsibility' in the body. How to work with a blockage or stagnated flow of energy at each chakra is shared in Chapter 9.

The anatomy of the energy body intertwines with your physical, mental, and emotional levels. Looking after this synergy and bringing it into balance promotes harmony and wellness at a whole new level.

Muladhara (Base) Chakra

The base chakra is located at the level of the tailbone; each chakra sits just outside the physical body. Its element is earth, its color is red, and it influences the sense of smell. Do you remember your grandmother's advice the first time you had to leave your newborn? Wrap the baby in your gown; your scent will calm your baby. And it worked. Your precious little one slept soundly while you were gone.

The base chakra influences emotions of safety, security, stability, steadiness, and confidence. It speaks to our primal urges to protect ourselves and our loved ones from harm. The organs associated with the base chakra are the kidneys, ureters, bladder, and adrenals. Muladhara is thought of as the battery of the body so it is important to care for this aspect to support our energy levels.

If you want to stimulate the base chakra, walk barefoot in nature, feel the connection on Mother Earth herself, and truly feel that you are part of nature, never separate. Contact with the earth refreshes and grounds you. Yoga poses good for the root chakra are the forward fold and butterfly.

Svadhisthana (Second) Chakra

This chakra is located at the level of the pelvis and affects the hips, reproductive organs, adrenal glands, gallbladder, and tongue. It links to the sense of taste, and is our social center, our center of relationships and connections.

It affects the pelvis, the reproductive system in women and men, and the connectivity downward to the hips, knees, and feet.

Its element is water and its color is orange. Its brightness symbolizes sensuality, sexuality, social connections, the ability to relax, and a good sense of self-worth. The second chakra brings out the inner child, joy, and creativity.

Manipura (Solar Plexus) Chakra

The solar plexus is located above the navel, below the breastbone in the upper abdomen; consequently, it supports the stomach and digestion system. It regulates the mid-back, liver, gallbladder, spleen, pancreas, stomach, and small and large intestines.

This center relates to working towards a goal or vision, willpower, determination, and inner strength. It is the center of your power and emotions, and at a refined level, surrender to a greater power.

It is the center of inner power. When unbalanced, this chakra contributes to the need to always be in control, inflexibility, and anxiety.

The element associated with the solar plexus is fire; its color is yellow.

Anahata (Heart) Chakra

The heart is a portal to the higher self, the reflection of the Soul in the body. By cultivating your conscious connection to the spiritual heart, nurturing yourself with loving kindness, and offering this unconditionally outward, you open this portal to your Soul's wisdom and deep knowing.

The heart is an established emotional center in Western culture and languages. The English language has many idioms referring to the heart: a heart of gold, eat your heart out, follow your heart, and a hundred more.

The heart chakra is found in the center of the chest at the breast-bone, and relates to the surrounding organs and tissues: the heart, lungs, circulation system, lymphatics, shoulders, arms, and hands. It is associated with the sense of touch. It is the fourth chakra, the bridge between the more physical lower chakras and the more refined and esoteric higher energy centers.

In contrast to what Westerners are used to, the associated color is not pink, but green. As expected, this chakra signifies unconditional love, unity, joy, forgiveness, and purity.

Stimulate this chakra by being kind, generous, forgiving, and honest. Give without expecting anything in return, offering with no agenda. People driven by this chakra often do charity work, love gardening, and spend time in nature.

Yoga poses (sphinx and melting heart) open the heart and are excellent for channeling heart energy to yourself and others.

Vishuddha (Throat) Chakra

As the English name indicates, this chakra is located in the throat. It relates to the vocal cords and voice, ears and hearing, and the upper parts of the lungs. The throat chakra is associated with your intuition and refined artistic talent.

The color of this chakra is sky blue. Singing, speaking your truth, and listening to others with sincerity stimulate the throat chakra.

Ajna (Third Eye) Chakra

The third eye between the eyebrows is nearly as well known as the heart chakra. It governs the pineal gland and reflects your ability to concentrate and maintain focus.

The color is a deep indigo blue, representing the ability to have and hold a vision and make it come true. The third eye is strengthened and balanced through focused meditation and visualization.

People with a strong and balanced Ajna chakra have a strong sense of knowing, and are visionaries with a great ability to manifest their dreams.

Sahasrara (Crown) Chakra

The seventh chakra is poetically known as the thousand-petalled lotus, and is violet or white. It sits just four inches above the head. It relates to the brain and to what is beyond our earthly experiences. It is the center of connection to Source.

Awakening and nurturing the crown chakra allows spiritual growth, greater joy, and peace derived from connection to all that is.

Yogis stimulate the crown chakra with headstands, meditation, chanting, and silence.

Quick Reminder

- The Chakra system represents the biofield of your body; this feeds your physical body and mental and emotional levels.
- The biofield communicates not only with your emotional, mental and physical dimensions but with the energy field of the those around you.
- Muladhara or the base chakra is found at the level of the tail bone, it grounds us and connects us to material possessions and can be thought of as the battery of the body.
- Svadhisthana or the second chakra is our social center, it helps us to feel good in our relationships and is an important center for our creativity.
- Manipura or the solar plexus is the energy center that governs our personal power, confidence and inner strength, it also is where our sense of humor lives.
- Anahata, the heart chakra is of course the center of love, purity and forgiveness; it is through the heart that we truly heal with deep self-love and acceptance.

- Vishudda, the energy center at the level of the throat is responsible for supporting us to speak our truth and to connect to our intuition.
- Ajna or the third eye supports keen focus and inner peace.
- Sahasrara at the crown connects us to Source, it is the center of Spiritual purity and connection to all that is.

2

Time is not the Enemy

> *Yesterday I was clever, so I wanted to change the world. Today I am wise, so I am changing myself.*

Rumi

Is Your Chaos Killing You?

LUCIA WAS one of the exhausted and stressed women from my days as a doctor in the busy family practice in London. We met again just when I was finalizing this book. I remembered her nervous energy from our brief meeting at my office, and her story confirmed my theory that sorting out practical details for some is the first step in self-healing.

Lucia's story

Michael forgot to tell me he had an early meeting and couldn't drop the kids off at school. Sarah, my go-to person in an emergency, had car trouble and sent her son Sammy over to catch a lift with my kids to school. The nanny arrived with a terrible cold, asked for cash to get medication, and left sneezing and coughing.

With four kids in the Uber, my office called. My budget meeting was moved forward by an hour as the CEO had to catch a flight.

It was crucial to attend the budget meeting. I had to negotiate the funding for new software. If we didn't get it soon, we would not meet a launch deadline in three months.

At the school gate, Sammy dropped the jar of mayonnaise his mom had promised for the burgers they were making in class that day. It landed on my new suede pumps, bought to show that I am a cool, calm, and collected department head. He cried and looked at me with worried eyes.

I honestly don't know whether I even cleaned the mess from my shoes. In the meeting, I remember my boss frowning, the CEO checking his watch every few minutes, and nausea gripping me for the rest of the day.

The headache built into a full migraine, the worst I'd had in months.

It turned out that the CEO won the golf tournament despite having to rush to catch the plane on its way to the luxury resort where it was being held. My boss approved the budget, but emailed the details about a workshop on time management. I read the details while the migraine pulsated behind my left eye, and nausea threatened to overtake me right there at my desk.

Time management, planning, setting goals? Pretty useless theory when people let you down and a jar of mayonnaise lands on you!

The incident was soon forgotten. Everybody was up in arms about another crisis —a delay at customs threatening the upgrading of office computer equipment.

I am telling you Lucia's Story to illustrate why she needed help with time management and a system in place to take care of herself and her responsibilities. She now looks brighter, the drawn look and eye bags had really softened. She told me that she uses a weekly plan on the fridge, including her and her husband's priorities and responsibilities. She regularly attends a dynamic yoga class and has even made some new friendship connections. Her health has improved, too. When we connected recently, she hadn't had one of her migraines in ages, and her stress levels were lower. She loves that a colleague recently commented on her graceful posture and that she looked so well.

Time Management When Life Happens

What does time management have to do with anxiety? Stress is, after all, a part of modern life.

Let us look at the differences between stress, anxiety, and over-thinking.

Stress is normal. Everybody is sometimes stressed, worried about, or fearing something. Stress is not necessarily bad; it can even motivate you to tackle and handle an unpleasant or difficult task. Once the worrying incident has passed, your stress usually subsides. However, when you are continuously stressed, it can get out of control and affect your daily life.

Anxiety is being in a state of worry or fear, and it is normal to feel anxious sometimes. But if it becomes persistent and interferes with daily life, you need to take action. You might avoid certain situations or experience physical reactions like an accelerated heart rate, shaking, and sweating. When anxiety gets to this stage, it clearly impacts behavior and can strain relationships. Some people withdraw from social events, others feel disconnected, and some feel overwhelmed by life. This book contains easy-to-follow techniques and practical advice for those who have the insight to recognize that you can manage anxiety holistically and start just where you are.

Overthinking about events of the past or things that may come to pass in the future, this mental activity can create a stressful state over the long term, a state of chronic stress and anxiety.

Stress tends to be short-term but can become chronic if we allow it; anxiety is a longer-term emotional state that stops us from functioning comfortably in our day-to-day lives. Lucia discovered she could limit her stress by preventing problems through time management, which helped to address her anxiety as well. For simplicity, we can think of stress as short-term worries, and anxiety and chronic stress as more of a long-term emotional state. Daily stress may build up to anxiety.

The truth about time management boils down to a simple equation: Time management equals less stress, and less stress equals less anxiety.

Of course, this is greatly simplified. Anxiety is often deeply embedded in our psyches, and is related to trauma or learned behaviors. Still, prolonged stress sends the body into fight-or-flight mode and aggravates anxiety. If you can limit your daily stress, you prevent the anxiety gremlin from becoming unmanageable.

This book covers many stress relief techniques: exercise, meditation, diet, and aromatherapy, to name but a few. Most of these techniques are not difficult or expensive, but all of them require time: Time to shop for nutritious ingredients, time to exercise, and time to meditate. If, like Lucia, you are spinning out of control even before your workday starts, plan to build in time for relaxation to offset the stresses of life, especially the unpredictable ones!

What Can Time Management Do for You?

If you Google definitions of time management, you will find most emphasize working more effectively and getting more done. I prefer a more holistic definition:

Time management is your tool to live a balanced life by organizing and planning the different priorities in your life. Proper time management can help you to work smart and be productive while having space for your loved ones and yourself.

Let us look at Lucia's predicament again. Even if she did plan her day and was a master in managing her time, she could not have managed the way her husband, friend, nanny, and Sammy with the mayonnaise jar behaved. All of these events were out of her control.

Lucia's real problem was that she never clearly formalized her priorities. Knowing your priorities is the first hurdle to cross when managing your time. Lucia was torn between her husband's forgetfulness, her nanny's cold, her neighbor's car problem, and the CEO's golfing trip.

Here's the beauty of priorities: They can move according to the challenges of the situation. Lucia's input at the budget meeting was a priority on that day. Had she planned the day before, she could have insisted that her husband postpone his meeting and drop the kids off at school. Alternatively, she could have offered to pay for the taxi and asked Sammy's mom to do the school run.

On another day, a sick or upset child could have been her priority, and she could have asked her assistant or boss to do the presentation.

Time management is much more than setting priorities. Still, it is a necessary point of departure.

Goal Setting

- Set your priorities for a specific timeframe, be it a day, a week, office hours, or free time.
- Set your goals according to your priorities. Remember, your priorities, and therefore your goals, can shift over time.
- List your tasks ranging from urgent to less urgent.
- Be realistic about your goals and your workload. Allow time for preparation, travel, attending to the task, wrapping it up, and formulating further actions.
- Have a proper break during your day. Distancing yourself from your work even for a few minutes gives perspective.
- At the end of the day, tick off the tasks you have completed.
- Investigate and invest in digital time management tools. Asana and Trello are great apps for keeping track of your projects and tasks.
- When setting your goals:

- Allow yourself a few minutes to clear your computer, desk, and mind.
- Delete irrelevant emails.
- File documents that are no longer relevant.
- Delegate less important and nagging tasks to an assistant.

Effective time control requires planning, recognizing priorities, setting goals, and evaluating performance and effectiveness. People who don't use these skills need to use their time effectively, which can result in disorganization. And so, they may underachieve at college, could be unproductive at their workplace, and chaos could well rule their private lives, leaving them emotionally stressed and overwhelmed with difficulty coping. These emotions often present as irritability, anger, sleeplessness, and anxiety.

The Benefits of Time Management at Work

Planning and goal setting tend to improve self-discipline, efficiency, and productivity. You are usually more focused when you realize what must be done in a limited time. It helps to have a dedicated time slot for lunch and regular shopping trips.

The most significant benefit of proper time management is that you become more focused and get more accomplished. The focus that comes through self-discipline contributes to delivering better quality work because you are not constantly distracted by your colleagues, phone, or considering dinner plans.

Being organized and focused will lessen stress, and when calmer, you will observe more, learn more, and be ready for the challenges and opportunities coming your way. Being overstressed and constantly in problem-solving mode does nothing to inspire confidence or signal efficiency to your colleagues and supervisors.

The Personal Benefits of Time Management

In an ideal world, we can separate our work and private lives, leaving work stress at the office and not thinking about personal things at work. Unfortunately, it is nearly impossible to separate our private and professional worlds completely. Most of us take our work stress home and our personal issues to work.

Once your workday feels more under control with these strategies, you will be calmer and more relaxed at home. It supports you and your loved ones to unwind and relax better, so your precious personal quality of life will improve because of bringing more structure to your work life.

The Gist of Goal Setting

Setting goals is intimately related to your priorities. Just like priorities, goals are not fixed; they change, get fulfilled, and sometimes have to be adapted.

If you are a drifter, like a forgotten dinghy on the ocean, chances are that you have yet to figure out where you want to go and thus have no goal. If you are a dreamer, your mind is probably planning the wonderful life waiting for you when your dream will become a reality. The dreamer often jumps to the end, but seldom plans the necessary in-between steps toward their final goal.

So, how do you set a goal? The dreamers have it right; they start at the end, but doers don't stop at the dream. They break their goals into smaller steps and work their way back to the beginning.

If you want to organize a concert with a world-famous band, break it down into practical steps. Get a budget for the event. Check the band's availability for a specific date. Agree and sign a contract. Book the venue for the date. Organize the marketing. You get my drift. Dreaming about ending the night with the band on the stage has no purpose unless you methodically work toward your dream.

The same principles apply to your personal life. Set your long-term goals and break them down into smaller, reachable goals.

A Last Thought: Perfectionism and People-Pleasing

When I think of the many women seeking help with anxiety, several share a tendency to be "perfect." Many looked wonderful and were meticulously dressed, even down to the fashionably-torn jeans and carefully constructed messy hairstyle. Family meals were balanced, and there were always fresh flowers in the family room. They were also the office mainstay, doing all those behind-the-scenes tasks to ensure the office ran smoothly.

Anabel was one of these women. She came to see me because of insomnia and feeling tired and irritable all the time. She felt unappreciated by her family and her colleagues. "They have no idea how hard I work, the private time I put in to do all the extras. My colleagues take the snacks I bring in for granted; my boss does not even read my weekly reports and never mentions the fresh flowers in reception."

Anabel's perfectionism and ingrained need to please caused her unnecessary stress. It was overwhelming her, leaving her feeling low and underappreciated. She was emotionally at a breaking point and felt helpless and unmotivated. Anabel was suffering from burnout. Her stress fed her anxiety, and she felt like she was spinning faster and faster in an endless circle of negativity.

She frowned when I asked whether her weekly reports were required by management. "Is writing these reports even listed in your job description? The snacks and the fresh flowers? Do you have a budget for them? Or do you buy them from your own pocket?"

Anabel did all these extras because she wanted to be perfect and needed the recognition to feel better about herself. The irony is Anabel was very successful at her job. She was the youngest manager in the company and had recently received a performance bonus based on her sales statistics.

Her drive for perfectionism stemmed from her childhood, she had to be the best in everything to make her busy professional parents proud, but her successes did not actually make her happy.

It took a while for Anabel to set her priorities at work: Running the sales section, not being the company's unpaid housekeeper.

Typical Anabel, she set priorities even for those unnecessary and unpaid tasks. She convinced the company to invest in software designed to select data from the system for monthly reports, and all staff members now use this software. Anabel delegated the responsibility for printer paper to a junior assistant. She has a budget for catering, and a budget for a florist to regularly dress the reception area with cut flowers.

Anabel lessened her work stress by facing her deep-seated emotional need for recognition. With this insight, she used her excellent planning skills and reorganized her work schedule. Now with some free time, she attends a weekly Pilates class during lunch, and even has a colorful set of matching pants and tops for every day of the week!

Anabel is still a perfectionist, but she now uses her skills to lessen her stress and recognize and manage her needs.

Quick Reminder

- Disorder around us causes stress and emotional upset. Effective time management is vital to sort out a chaotic lifestyle.
- Attaching value to time indicates respect for yourself and other people.
- Establishing personal and professional priorities goes a long way in tackling stress.
- Setting realistic goals is essential in time management.
- Break goals down into smaller steps. Completing every small step gives an immediate sense of achievement, motivating you to continue.
- Some personality types find it more difficult than others to manage their time. However, you can learn this skill: how to prioritize, set goals, and complete tasks on time. In time, you will feel the benefit of more structure and how it gives you more freedom!

An organized daily schedule is a practical starting point for the overwhelmed and stressed woman. If you have fewer decisions to make over the day because your day is planned out, you will be calmer at work and home, sleep better, and feel better. It's the logical first practical step to curb anxiety.

3

Rest and Rejuvenate

> *It is a common experience that a problem difficult at night is resolved in the morning after the committee of sleep has worked on it.*

John Steinbeck

Mind Too Busy For Sleep?

MEGAN WAS A STRONG GIRL; a born leader with vision and ambition. She took responsibility for her younger siblings' emotional security from an early age. Her parents had regular screaming matches—their way of relieving tension, but devastating for the children. Although never physically violent, their frequent arguments and highly-expressed emotions deeply upset and frightened the children.

A child herself, Megan fled with her siblings whenever the fights started. She read stories to distract them. They had special hideaways: In summer, a shady spot in the garden, and as the cold weather set in, the attic. Both parents apologized and held each other and the children in tearful embraces when things calmed down. It was forgiven and forgotten, except for Megan, who remained stoical and outwardly calm, training herself from a young age to bottle up her emotions to stay strong for her siblings.

She spent most nights tossing and turning. Thoughts spun endlessly as she relived the fights, and her mind created potential catastrophic outcomes for her family because of these overheard arguments. She woke up frequently, rarely getting more than three hours of continuous sleep.

When she did eventually fall asleep, she woke up every few minutes. She was continuously exhausted.

Not surprisingly, Megan continued her role as a protector at school, calling out the bullies and taking the lead in activities. She was an achiever, always leading from the front. But at night, Megan found it increasingly difficult to sleep. She was so exhausted that she accepted it as her normal state.

One morning in her late teens, Megan's mother found her unresponsive, an empty bottle of sleeping pills beside her.

Fortunately, Megan made a full recovery, and what she was going through came to light. After this episode, Megan took steps to heal and this had a positive outcome for her and her family.

Family counseling addressed the cause of Megan's anxiety. She needed to find safe and comfortable ways to express herself and not allow complex and valid emotions to be buried. She learned relaxation techniques that relieved her pent-up stress and anxiety, and gradually improved her sleep quality.

Insomnia and poor mental health are closely related. Scientists connect sleeping issues to anxiety, depression, bipolar disorder, and other mental health issues. While psychologists previously believed mental health issues caused insomnia, they now say the reverse is also true: Long-term poor sleep contributes to mental distress and anxiety.

It seems like the proverbial chicken-or-egg situation, but improving sleep quality can break this cycle. Let us take a closer look at the brain during sleep, and then find out how to sleep better.

While You Are Sleeping

From Chapter 1, we know that brain activity continues during sleep. However, this activity fluctuates during the different stages of sleep. In some stages, brain activity decreases, and in others, it picks up again. To rest and restore the brain and the body, you have to cycle through the four stages of sleep several times a night. Every phase contributes in its own way to the recharging of the body and the brain.

The Sleep Cycle

Scientists call our sleeping cycles sleep architecture. Under ideal sleeping conditions, the cycle is repeated up to five or six times during the recommended eight hours of sleep, each contributing uniquely to the healing of the body and brain. Constant lack of sleep impacts physical and emotional health and cognitive function.

Age, alcohol, drugs, and some physical and mental health conditions can negatively affect sleep stages and cycles. Unfortunately, an unhealthy sleep pattern is challenging (but not impossible) to break.

The 4 Stages of the Sleep Cycle

Stage 1 (N1) takes one to five minutes. In this stage, you doze off, drifting between awareness and sleep as your brain activity slows down. However, as you have yet to fall asleep fully, if you are disturbed and woken up, you might struggle to doze off again. Some people move to stage two very quickly, but those suffering from insomnia struggle to move out of stage one.

Stage 2 (N2) takes 10 to 60 minutes. The body is deeply relaxed, body temperature drops, and the breathing and heart rate slow down. During stage two, the brain has short bursts of activity. Scientists say these activity flares help to protect the brain from being woken up by external disturbances during this stage.

Stage 3 (N3) takes 20 to 40 minutes and is the period of deep sleep. The body relaxes further, and breathing and heart rate decrease even more.

The brain activity during this time is predominantly delta waves, essential for rest and recovery. The immune system is also restored during stage three, which is vital for physical health.

The earlier part of the night is the best for deep sleep and longer periods. As the night progresses, and in later cycles, stage three gets shorter and shorter, emphasizing how important it is to sleep for at least eight hours.

Stage 4 (REM Sleep) lasts 10 to 60 minutes. Your brain activity picks up during this stage. Usually, you go into REM (rapid eye movement) after about 90 minutes of sleep. Although the eyelids are closed, the eyes move rapidly. Except for your eyes, the muscles in your body are temporarily paralyzed.

We dream in all sleep stages, but our REM dreams are usually more vivid. This stage is vital for cognitive function: memory, learning, advanced thought processes, and creativity.

Babies often spend more time in REM sleep than adults, and older adults have shorter periods of REM sleep.

Sleep and Mental Health

Healthy sleep patterns, and specifically sufficient sleep during the fourth stage, the REM sleep stage, are essential for the brain to process emotional information. When the first three sleeping stages are disturbed, you don't sleep long enough for the brain to work through the previous day's thoughts, memories, and emotions. This processing of thoughts and feelings is vital to find emotional balance.

When the subconscious mind cannot process events, memories, and emotions during sleep, we can become moody, overly emotionally sensitive, low in mood, anxious, and even have thoughts of self-harm.

Global statistics on depression reflect how common this problem is. Although disturbing, these statistics help to destigmatize mental health issues. Where previously, people with mental health conditions refrained from talking about it, society now has more understanding of these issues.

A constant lack of sleep reinforces depression, but long-term exhaustion can also contribute to and deepen the depression. Whichever came first, the chicken or the egg, you can address depression symptoms by improving sleep quality. Good sleep does not magically erase depression, but it can complement any medical treatment and counseling designed to treat it.

Anxiety disorders present as fear and worry, and may be a part of different, more specific patterns such as social anxiety, panic disorder, obsessive-compulsive behavior, and post-traumatic stress. Anxiety can impact the quality of life and, for many, causes high levels of distress, although this pain is often hidden.

When, like Megan, you manage to hide your anxiety, it usually catches up with you at bedtime. Your worries, fears, and overthinking take center stage, and your mind goes into overdrive just as you want to settle into sleep. You might be exhausted, but your mind just can't shut down, and you struggle to fall asleep. If you struggle to fall asleep or stay asleep, your mind will not progress through the necessary sleep stages and it is likely that you will wake up exhausted in body and mind. When this happens night after night, your anxiety can spiral out of control, as you will start to worry about not getting enough sleep the next night. It can create a problematic cycle of sleep anxiety (worry that you won't sleep, stopping you from sleeping) if you don't take steps to break it.

It is essential to realize that your mental health and sleep are interrelated: Improve the one, and the other will benefit. Start with the techniques and advice in this chapter, but don't hesitate to get professional help if necessary.

More Benefits of Better Sleep

A good night's rest not only improves your mood and emotional well-being, but your body also benefits in several ways.

- Weight: You might be surprised to learn that weight and proper sleep go hand in hand. Yes, your lack of sleep might add to the padding around your belly. When your body craves sleep, it increases the hunger hormone ghrelin. Ghrelin causes food cravings, typically food high in carbohydrates and fat, such as pastries, pizza, chips, and chocolate.

- Appetite Hormones: In addition to larger quantities of ghrelin, the sleep-deprived body releases less leptin. Leptin is the hormone that causes you to feel full and, thus, less hungry. It is a double whammy: A lack of sleep releases hormones that increase your appetite and decrease hormones to signal you have had enough to eat!

- Cognitive Function: Good sleep, especially REM sleep, improves your cognitive processes. Do you remember your mother insisting that you go to bed early on a school night? It is not only because a tired child is often difficult, and she wanted some peace. Being exhausted limits concentration and performance. When rested, one's problem-solving abilities and academic performance are significantly better.

- Social Interactions: Sleep deprivation can lead to a lack of self-control and anti-social behavior. Exhausted people withdraw from family events and avoid friends and social gatherings.

- Physical Performance: A tired body cannot perform ultimately; every athlete knows that proper rest is a prerequisite for athletic excellence. Additionally, you are more prone to injuries when tired; fine motor skills are compromised, reaction time slows down, and muscles are weaker. Tiredness also negatively affects the motivation to persevere and complete a race or a game.

- <u>Heart Health and High Blood Pressure</u>: Too little sleep can contribute to heart disease and high blood pressure. Typically, blood pressure drops during deep sleep, enhancing the body's ability to stabilize blood pressure.
- <u>Sugar and Type 2 Diabetes</u>: Sleep-deprived people tend to crave and consume foods high in fat and carbohydrate (sugars). These could be significant contributors to high blood pressure and becoming overweight. High sugar consumption contributes to poor blood sugar balance, insulin resistance, and eventually type 2 diabetes. When the body is exhausted, chronic, background low-grade inflammation sets in, and hormonal changes occur, putting the physical body under stress. Type 2 diabetes is a condition that impacts the whole body, including circulation, nerves, and the immune system.
- <u>Immune System</u>: Proper sleep, especially stage three deep sleep, is necessary to boost the body's immune system, which is vital for your body's defense from pathogens like viruses and bacteria in the environment.
- <u>Inflammation</u>: Chronic low-grade inflammation contributes to the body's susceptibility to illnesses such as obesity, heart disease, digestive disorders, certain types of cancer, Alzheimer's disease, depression, type 2 diabetes, poor skin quality, and premature aging.

People living with insomnia can succumb to anxiety about not sleeping, leading to more overthinking and a vicious cycle of being too anxious to sleep. If you regularly experience sleeping issues, the following section will help improve your sleep quality. As your sleep patterns improve, you will also have the energy to address your underlying emotional issues and worries.

How to Improve Sleep Quality

If you wish to sleep better, start with your routine leading up to bedtime. Take the time to prepare your body, and mind for sleep. Tackling practical things you can control is a good starting point. Once you have your bedtime routine in order, you have laid a foundation for sound sleep.

Reset Your Natural Rhythm

When it comes to sleep, routine assists your body in regulating its circadian rhythm. The circadian rhythm is the body's natural sleep-wake cycle, managed by a series of hormones. A fixed routine works with the body's primal rhythm: when to be active, when to eat, time to digest food, time to relax its muscles and nerves, and time to sleep.

Your life is probably a race from one thing to the next, with hundreds of demands and dilemmas flashing through your mind every day. It is exactly why a routine when you get home could support you in switching gears. You don't have to make drastic changes. Start with small tweaks, like going to bed at the same time every night. Try to have a fixed dinner time at least three hours before bedtime. The digestive system takes time, and a big meal might keep you awake. Start your downtime with a proper sit-down dinner to signal to your body and mind that it is time to slow down.

Routine tasks like cleaning the kitchen, preparing lunch boxes, and finding time to do something you enjoy and find relaxing (maybe walking the dog or chatting with a friend), can help distance you from the day's events. Feed the cat and put the kids to bed—phone your mother. Do whatever you need to do. However, when it comes to the 30--60 minutes before bed, aim to start winding down with no interruptions; this is your time.

Spruce up Your Bedtime Routine

Allow 30–60 minutes to prepare yourself for bed. Show your love by avoiding caffeine (such as coffee, black tea, green tea, or sodas) from lunchtime onward. If you have a history of insomnia, you can opt for caffeine-free alternatives like Rooibos tea or chicory coffee alternatives. Also, avoid alcohol. You might think alcohol calms your nerves and makes you sleepy. The initial relaxation wears off quickly, sleep tends to be light, and you will be more prone to frequent waking overnight.

Electronic devices at bedtime can be a menace. It's best not to have any devices in your bedroom. Think about it; electronic devices bring the world and its problems into your bedroom. Don't check work emails; let your boss and the rest of the world wait until the morning. There's very little you can do at night anyhow. Allow yourself a break from all electronics. Charge them in a different part of the house and allow sleep to recharge your batteries.

It is now known that the blue light from screens and even small charging lights interferes with good sleep.

Make sure your bedside clock is not emitting light. An analog clock with glow-in-the-dark hands is ideal to avoid sleep disturbance and the harshness of checking your phone screen for the time at night.

The busier you are, the more important a bedtime routine is. Your mind and brain are probably overloaded by the stresses of the day. Consequently, your body needs cues to indicate it is time to slow down and rest. By performing the same tasks every night at the same time, your body and mind settle into a new pattern and a new habit of letting go of the day's rush and moving into rest.

Remember your bedtime routines as a child? Playing in the bath with your toys, soft pajamas, a favorite soft toy, and a bedtime story. Your parents often repeated the same story, and you never tired of it because it wasn't the story but the caring and security that put you to sleep.

Try to create a relaxing atmosphere in your bedroom. Use muted, calm colors in your bedroom decor. Get a soft blanket or pillow, and enjoy the relaxing scent of your body cream, perhaps with lavender to support your sleep with scent. Invest in small luxuries like soft organic cotton bedding and thick curtains to block out the daylight. Some people do really well with a weighted blanket (start with the lightest weight and make sure it does not weigh on your chest or neck at night). Bringing these into your bedtime routine will give you a sense of stability, comfort, and security.

If you are too alert for sleep, try gentle yoga stretches, meditation, reading (not on a screen, and nothing too exciting or activating, especially not the news), or listening to a deep sleep audio track. These prepare the body for sleep.

Keep a gratitude journal. Think of five things every day for which you are grateful and record them. It helps to program your incredible subconscious mind with gratitude for what is, and as your subconscious mind makes 95% of your choices every day, wouldn't it be great to program it with an attitude of gratitude?

I have included a free bonus sleep audio track with this book; it is based on the full body relaxation at the end of a yoga class, the Savasana, and is laced with sleep-supporting energy medicine. Use the QR code below to access the resource and the coupon code Self-HealingGift to access it for free:

Pamper Your Body

Your cat purrs when you stroke it. Your house is more inviting after cleaning and adding some fresh flowers. The shop assistant's face lights up when you ask about her grandchildren. Similarly, your body responds to care and will eventually reward you with refreshing sleep.

Enjoy a relaxing bath or shower, pampering your skin and brushing your hair. Tell your body you appreciate it and allow your body to rest and rejuvenate.

Make Your Bedroom a Haven

It might seem obvious, but does your bedroom invite sleep? Do you work or study in bed? Stop bringing these energies into your sleep space. Make it a haven of peace and deep sleep.

Is it calm and quiet or brightly lit? Do you and your partner habitually pick fights in the privacy of your bedroom to not upset the children? Or do you use bedtime to re-live the day's problems?

Keep toxic behaviors away from your bedroom sanctuary, and let it be your haven of peace.

Don't Wait for Sleep Indefinitely

Have you done all the above and still struggle to fall asleep? Chapter six describes a few interesting techniques to get rid of anxiety and help us fall asleep. Most importantly, don't get yourself all worked up.

Get out of bed when you get stressed because sleep keeps escaping you. Don't start working or cleaning the kitchen. Instead, read something mundane and non-stimulating until you are sleepy, and then try dozing off. Keep the lights low; bright lights are activating. You can use the sleep audio track above to give your mind something to follow into deep relaxation, letting intrusive thoughts or concerns fall away.

Get Rid of the Mind's Monkey Chatter

Does your mind race? Are worries cluttering up your thoughts?

Zen Buddhists describe the chaotic mind clutter as monkey chatter, comparing it to monkeys endlessly chattering while jumping up and down and swinging from tree to tree. We know this as the ego, the personality often raking over the day, worrying about events past and those to come. The kind of brainwaves in action here are beta—these are our regular day-to-day activity brainwaves, and we need to slow them down to the slower alpha brainwaves to sleep. In an alpha brainwave state, there are fewer thoughts and more presence for integration of the day's events.

How can you get rid of the residue of the day's stresses? Your difficulties and worries are real and can't just be wished away or forgotten. You will find several techniques and exercises in the second part of this book. Study them, practice them, and make them part of your lifestyle.

But sometimes, we need a quicker solution, something that can help on those difficult sleepless nights when our messy minds just can't calm down. The key to calming your mind and stopping the monkey chatter is not trying to push your worries to the back of your mind. Instead, face them and dump them. The following tool will help you get a bit of distance between your fears and your mind; furthermore, it could help you with your time management planning the next day.

This helpful tool is called brain dumping, or more generally known as "writing your pages." When you write your pages, it helps you to drop everything whirring around your mind. Put pen to paper and just keep writing. Whatever comes—worries, jokes, song lyrics, whatever is cluttering up your headspace, get it onto paper and out of your way! Don't worry about order, or categories, or solutions. You are not planning here; you are not formulating solutions; you are merely dumping the tangled mess in your mind onto paper. Writing pages is not the same as journaling. Both have a place in the self-healing of anxiety. You can find more information on journaling in Chapter 8.

It seems silly that you can rid yourself of real worries and deeply-rooted negative emotions by writing them down. Let's look at how and why brain dumping works, though. Writing pages works because your worries take on a different identity when reconstructing them into formal letters and words on paper. It brings some distance between your mind and the words.

In dumping these worries outside your brain, your body gradually moves from fight-or-flight to resting mode. Your problems have not disappeared magically, but you view them more realistically. It helps you realize that your concerns can wait until the next day.

Take the Menace out of Menopause

Perimenopause and menopause contribute to sleeping problems because a woman's hormones fluctuate during these stages. Unbalanced estrogen levels affect the body and emotions. It can cause mood swings, hot flashes, weight gain, digestive issues, and sleep problems.

These symptoms can affect a woman's confidence and self-image, which add even more stress. It is a normal transition for all women. You can support your body to move through this time of change gracefully.

Unfortunately, mood swings and sleep issues are not the only problems during menopause. Sleep apnea often plagues women, and many are unaware that it contributes to their insomnia. It is a condition where breathing stops several times overnight. Sleep apnea contributes to health conditions, such as heart failure and high blood pressure, so it's essential to recognize if it affects you.

Women who are overweight with more fat around the neck and jaw are more likely to develop sleep apnea, especially combined with menopause. A partner often notices it as snoring and then long pauses between snores.

If you suffer from poor sleep and think that sleep apnea might be a problem for you, use these free online assessments to help to identify whether obstructive sleep apnea could be present and whether it is time to see your doctor:

http://stopbang.ca/osa/screening.php

https://www.blf.org.uk/support-for-you/obstructive-sleep-apnoea-osa/diagnosis/epworth-sleepiness-scale

Your doctor can help with sleep apnea and other menopausal symptoms. You can get help, sleep better, and have a better quality of life. The advice above, especially the techniques in the book's second half, will help you. A holistic approach is the best way to address menopause symptoms, which can affect many facets of life.

It's Not Working!

Are the tips above not working for you?

You introduced some routine into your day and evening. You removed most of the clutter from your bedroom and created a sleep sanctuary. You have banned your phone from the bedroom and have stopped nighttime scrolling or email checking. You do brain dumping, but still struggle to doze off.

Firstly, give yourself a break. Remember, your sleeping disturbances did not start suddenly. They were a long time in the making, and the only way to establish a healthy sleeping pattern is to persevere. Give your body and mind time to re-adjust. Persevere with the positive changes.

In part two, this book will reinforce the practical changes that will support your self-healing. You started with time management, a practical method to bring order to the chaos of your daily schedule. This chapter guides you to master your sleep problems. The next chapter shows you to better understand your body and why self-acceptance, care, and self-worth are necessary to break free of anxiety and bring balance back to your body, mind, heart, and Soul.

Quick Reminder

- The brain cycles through different phases while we are asleep, which are necessary for cognitive function, creativity, and memory.
- Consistent sleep deprivation impacts physical health, emotional well-being, and cognitive function.
- Depression and anxiety can cause sleep problems, and lack of sleep worsens depression and anxiety.
- You must go through the sleep cycle several times a night to benefit the most from sleep.
- Each cycle has four stages, and each stage contributes in a specific way to restore the body and brain.
- A holistic, natural approach to sleeping problems includes several practical steps you can take to improve your sleep.

Use the deep sleep audio, designed to relax your body for sleep and laced with energy medicine to support rejuvenating rest. Use the "brain dumping" technique to get your many thoughts onto paper, creating a space conducive to sleep.

4

Your Body, Your Temple

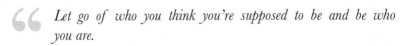

> *Let go of who you think you're supposed to be and be who you are.*
>
> Brené Brown

Body Image

BODY POSITIVITY IS A RELATIVELY new movement that, among others, challenges society's values about body shape. The campaign slams social media for supporting body shaming and promotes acceptance of the body in all shapes and sizes.

Unfortunately, being positive about your body is not that straightforward. Even though they might support the body-positive movement, most women have at least a couple of hang-ups about their bodies. To the outsider, these issues might seem insignificant, but still, many women would like to change some aspect of their appearance: curly hair, thin hair, "thunder thighs", skinny legs, nose shape, or chest size.

Experts suggest that as part of accepting our bodies, we should also learn to appreciate the fantastic way our bodies function. Our bodies are incredibly complex: The brain contains around 86 billion neurons, specially designed to communicate with every other cell in the body through electrical messages (Voytek, 2013).

We are so used to taking our bodies for granted that we don't even realize the intricate workings of our organs, muscles, digestion, sight, hearing, and more. There is so much that modern science is still discovering about how this amazing temple we each reside in functions.

External factors, such as the Body Positivity movement, may, over time, change society's attitude, but we have a long way to go. If you have a negative body image that contributes to your anxiety, read on. This chapter will help you address negative perceptions of your body and help you to integrate healthy self-love and self-confidence into your psyche step by step.

Learning to Accept Yourself

Social Media: Two-sided Coin

The reality is that perhaps the facts about our wonderful bodies and Body Positivity don't help much when you compare your (perceived) flaws with a celebrity's pictures. Take heart in knowing that most of the time, the images have been stretched and photoshopped to show that celebrity in their most idealized form, not forgetting the hours spent in the makeup chair just before the picture was taken! Most stars have a professional team to polish their looks for the camera: personal trainers, hairdressers, make-up artists, fashion designers, and stylists. The celebrity look is a carefully constructed piece of marketing to convey a message of perfection to sell an image that is simply unattainable because it does not exist to begin with. Perfection, even though mostly faked, is the foundation for a celebrity's fame.

How do these media images affect you? Do you feel fat? Too short? Not good enough? For those of us that can feel unworthy and unattractive at times, comparing ourselves to these unrealistic images can be brutal and fuel low, anxious feelings.

Broaden Your Horizons and Change Your Thoughts

There's nothing wrong with following celebrities and influencers and being inspired by them. But consider how we compare ourselves to unreal, impossible, and faked beauty "ideals." Contemplate how often you find yourself seeking validation from external sources.

How do you feel about yourself on the inside? What qualities do you love about yourself? What qualities do you love about those close to you? Whom do you admire, and why? What could you do to cultivate those qualities you see in others in your own incredible temple?

Body Care and Appreciation

Psychologists tell us to accept our bodies, flaws and all. But how do you take the first step to acceptance of yourself physically? Try a side step: Self-worth and accepting yourself are intimately related. It's often easier to start concentrating on the positives in your life. Write out a list of your good qualities and truly allow yourself to spend some time appreciating them. What would your loved ones say to describe you? This exercise will help to give you perspective and accept that it is okay to have shortcomings.

We often find it difficult to concentrate on the positive when stressed. On your journey of self-healing anxiety, you might hit a roadblock, a point of feeling stuck, or low; this is normal. Use this event to remind yourself of what you have learned thus far. Celebrate yourself and the positive changes that have been made, that you have started a journey, taken the initiative to empower yourself, knowing that this path may have twists and turns. If necessary speak to your doctor, trusted friend, or therapist to get the support you need to continue moving forward.

Part of accepting your body is caring for it. Exercise is an essential part of caring for and appreciating your body. In the next section, you will learn how important exercise is—not to lose weight or change your shape to adhere to society's standards—but to improve your mental and physical health.

Physical Activity and Anxiety

We know that exercise helps with physical health and weight management. Exercise also helps with mental health. The more you care for your body, the more you will discover how wonderfully complex your body is. Let us look at the link between exercise, endorphins, and emotional health. The word endorphin combines endogenous (internal origin) and morphine (an opioid pain reliever), which hints at the endorphin's role in our bodies.

During exercise, the body perceives physical activity as increased stress and exertion. The brain releases feel-good hormones, endorphins, to help the body cope with the expected pain during recovery.

Because of the release of feel-good hormones during exercise, our tension and mood swings decrease, and our sleep quality improves. Consequently, our self-esteem and confidence also improve.

You may find that anxiety makes it difficult to start a regular exercise habit. There may be hesitancy when meeting new people, and perhaps you associate a physical challenge with feeling stressed out. Having a negative body image complicates matters further.

The good news is that you can exercise in the privacy of your own home or immediate neighborhood. You don't need special clothes or equipment, and you don't have to join a gym or a club. Start with a brisk walk around the block. Studies have proven that walking for 10 minutes gives the same stress relief as working out for 45 minutes (*Exercising for Stress and Anxiety*, n.d.). If you really want to stay at home, put on your favorite music and dance; just move your body for you. Bringing movement and dynamism to your day can lift your spirits.

The same applies to swimming, running, yoga, and other mild forms of exercise. More and more doctors include exercise in treatment programs for anxiety.

Exercise for Your Health, Not your Appearance

Remember, this section on exercise concentrates on ways to lessen anxiety, not to improve your appearance. You may also lose weight, but that will be a bonus.

Increased fitness strengthens positive emotions and improves mood and sleep. You will get your spark back. The trick is to find something you enjoy and stick with it: cycling, swimming, or dancing, for example. You'll find that increasing your weekly activity improves your flexibility and strength, and can improve your social life, too!

Getting Motivated

If you're making changes to your lifestyle, but still have times when you feel vulnerable and worries creep back, how do you stick with the positive changes? The answer is step by step, and one day at a time.

Don't start with unrealistic goals, like running for an hour straight right away. Start with a simple goal. Walk for 10 minutes, and increase the time and the pace gradually. Regular exercise will boost the release of feel-good endorphins, and your energy and mood will gradually pick up.

Choose an enjoyable activity. Walk in your local park and make mental notes of the trees, flowers, or pleasing architecture on your route. You might even find a neighbor you can join to walk the dog and share your love of nature.

Remember to congratulate yourself on making these changes, and record your gratitude daily in your journal.

<u>Understand What Motivates You</u>

At some point on your journey back to balance, you might reach a plateau and lose interest. Understanding how motivation works will help you conquer this temporary hiccup in your plans to change. Motivation stems from outside (external) or inside (intrinsic) factors.

External motivation typically involves rewards: a prize, money, or promotion. Intrinsic motivation does not include a reward from somebody else. It stems from your will to do something for yourself. For example, if you read this book to discover how to self-heal your anxiety, your motivation is intrinsic.

Intrinsic motivation can have its own rewards; thus, when you realize the novelty has worn off your exercise, it's time to reinforce your intrinsic motivation. Reflect on why you started this journey to find better health. Go back to your notes, and notice the positive changes you have achieved so far.

Write down the goals you have already achieved. Set new goals when you feel discouraged and low. Challenge yourself to move to the next level in your program, or investigate new exercise possibilities. If you have only walked in your neighborhood, it might be time to join a hiking club. You have come further than you think; cross the hurdles and explore the new opportunities awaiting you on the other side.

The Story of Blood Sugar and Mood

Blood sugar levels influence your long-term health, energy levels, ability to concentrate, and mood. To understand how glucose can affect mood, let us look at the crucial role glucose plays in our bodies.

<u>Glucose in the Body</u>

- Glucose is the primary fuel source for the body and is necessary for all body and brain functions.
- Blood carries glucose to each and every cell in the body.

- Glucose is a sugar. All carbohydrates are broken down to glucose through digestion.
- The pancreas releases two entirely different hormones that help regulate glucose levels:
- Insulin reduces the amount of glucose in the bloodstream by storing away excess sugars when detected.
- Glucagon tells the liver to release sugar to stabilize blood sugar levels. (Glucagon is a hormone, and glucose is a sugar —an energy source; they're easily confused.)
- Insulin resistance occurs when the body's cells do not respond to insulin appropriately, causing elevated blood sugar levels.
- Type 2 diabetes occurs when blood sugar levels are consistently too high and follows after insulin resistance develops.

Glucose and Emotions

Your state of physical health will significantly impact your emotions. Therefore, keeping tabs on inflammation, a healthy gut, resilience to stress, a healthy thyroid, and stable blood sugar levels improve your emotional well-being.

Difficulty concentrating, irritability, and tiredness might be symptoms of low blood sugar swings, although we read them as emotional issues.

The recently coined word "hangry" describes the emotions of someone with hypoglycemia: hunger, anger, irritability, and intense sugar cravings. There are different types of hypoglycemia:

- *Reactive hypoglycemia* (or a sugar crash) occurs when sugar levels fall dramatically about two hours after a meal or snack. It usually happens if you have had a high-sugar or refined carbohydrate snack, like a jelly donut or chocolate bar.

- Fasting hypoglycemia happens when your blood sugar levels fall because of an extended fasting period.

But let's concentrate on the link between blood sugar and emotions. Fluctuations in blood sugar levels correspond with negative emotions, stress, and anxiety. So let us look at what happens when the body is under stress:

- In the adrenal glands, adrenaline is released and this affects the metabolism to increase blood glucose levels.
- Through the sympathetic nervous system, the body adopts the fight-or-flight (stress) response (blood pressure and heart rate increase, you feel sweaty, your pupils dilate, and digestion slows as blood supply increases to your muscles).
- The stress hormone cortisol is also released. Cortisol disrupts glucose metabolism and causes even more blood glucose fluctuations.

How to Balance Blood Glucose Levels and Improve Your Mood

Our bodies and brains need a stable supply of glucose to function optimally. Those seemingly insignificant decisions we make daily about what we eat and how we live accumulate and play a major role in glucose metabolism and our long-term metabolic health.

Diet

The best way to maintain healthy blood sugar levels is by bringing awareness to the balance of carbohydrates/sugars (e.g., bread, rice, potatoes, sweet treats), healthy fats (e.g., olive oil, coconut oil), and lean protein (e.g., turkey, tofu, egg) in your diet. Refined carbohydrates are metabolized to sugar very quickly in the body, so reducing the amount of white rice, pasta, and bread that you eat will help you to balance your blood sugar over the day. Seriously consider cutting sugary snacks and drinks from your diet altogether.

Food high in fiber, such as wholegrains, vegetables, nuts (apart from peanuts), and fruit, contain glucose and other nutrients necessary for your health and digestive processes. These types of food take time to digest and therefore, release glucose more slowly, thus preventing high blood sugar spikes followed by a sugar crash. The body needs longer and takes more energy to break them down and release the sugars within. They tend to keep you feeling fuller for longer after eating them.

Like body cells, brain cells do not function optimally when glucose levels are too high or fluctuate too often. Healthy fats are vital for the brain's optimal function. Using small amounts of olive and coconut oil in your cooking and eating avocados and nuts like almonds and walnuts will support your brain health because these contain good amounts of healthy fats.

Blood sugar imbalances are related to obesity, anxiety and depression, and emotional health conditions like depression. Researchers report that sugar cravings, fatigue, hyper-sensitivity, and a feeling of heaviness are symptoms related to blood sugar imbalances.

<u>Drinking Enough Water</u>

Water makes up about 70% of your body weight, and every part of the body needs water to function (*Are You Drinking Enough Water*, n.d.).

Have you ever developed a severe headache when not taking in enough fluids? Your brain cells become dehydrated when that happens. Something as simple as drinking enough water helps brain cells to function correctly. It also stabilizes your emotions, and can even support weight loss. Usually, the right amount is around six to eight glasses of water per day; more if you are in a hot climate or physically active.

<u>Proper Sleep Regulates Hormones</u>

A lack of sleep upsets the body's hormonal balance, starting with increased cortisol production. Cortisol affects the body's blood sugar regulation, which can result in poor dietary choices. Fatigue and exhaustion from a lack of sleep affect insulin resistance, and even more stress hormones are released.

Good sleep is a non-negotiable for emotional and physical health, especially in regulating glucose release and metabolism.

Foods to Regulate Healthy Glucose Levels

You can eat foods to improve your health. We know that refined carbohydrates and sugary foods cause spikes in blood sugar. Let us look at the foods that regulate blood sugar.

- <u>Vegetables</u>

The colloquial saying "Familiarity breeds contempt" can apply to "Eat your greens." We have heard it so often and then ignored the advice. I have included some key points about some food sources below, describing their myriad benefits:

Broccoli contains sulforaphane, a bioactive compound with anti-diabetic properties. Sulforaphane sharpens the body's insulin sensitivity, and thus brings down glucose levels.

Broccoli and broccoli sprouts are most beneficial when eaten raw or lightly steamed. Add mustard seed to broccoli to even further enhance its nutritional value.

Kale is a superfood because it contains fiber and flavonoid antioxidants. The antioxidants in kale sharpen insulin sensitivity and help lower glucose levels.

Pumpkin and pumpkin seeds are on the other side of the vegetable color charts. Pumpkin has polysaccharides (complex carbohydrates) that are excellent for regulating blood sugar. Also, pumpkin seeds contain healthy fats, minerals like zinc and magnesium, plus protein, so glucose is released over a longer time.

- <u>Fruit</u>

That juicy apple may indeed help to keep the doctor away. It contains several soluble fibers, which release glucose slower, preventing spikes in blood sugar. Eating apples and blueberries regularly may help to reduce the risk of type 2 diabetes. Eating an apple or red raspberries about 30 minutes before a meal of refined carbohydrates may limit the blood sugar spikes that follow. Stewed apple (applesauce without added sugar) with the skins on, and perhaps with a good dash of cinnamon or cloves, has beneficial properties for gut health and repair.

Citrus fruits regulate blood sugar in more than one way. Their sugar does not cause spikes like the sugars of some other fruits. Also, citrus fruit's natural fiber contains plant compounds with anti-diabetic properties.

Berries are another favorite, as research has shown they have properties that help our blood sugars to stay level even after eating refined carbohydrates. Plus, they are packed with antioxidants, vitamins, minerals, fiber, and phytonutrients. So eat plenty of fresh or frozen berries like strawberries, blueberries, and blackberries to help you control your blood sugar.

Avocados are fruit, although we use them in salad. Whatever way you have your avocado, they are packed with good fats, fiber, vitamins, and minerals, and are excellent for stabilizing glucose in the blood.

Okra, also known as a vegetable, is another fruit with polysaccharides, antioxidants, and compounds that help regulate blood sugar.

- Eggs

Eggs are nearly a perfectly balanced meal, with protein, good fat, vitamins, minerals, and antioxidants. Regularly eating eggs can improve insulin sensitivity and lowers the risk of diabetes.

- Fermented Foods

Fermented food is especially good for lowering blood sugar. During the fermentation process, probiotics form naturally. Probiotics help absorb carbohydrates, which cause blood sugar spikes. They support your gut's microbiome, the "rainforest" of microorganisms that perform thousands of tasks for your body, eliminating toxins and manufacturing vital messenger proteins to defend the body as a big part of the body's immune system. Therefore, a small portion of kefir, yogurt, kimchi, or sauerkraut goes a long way to promote gut health, lower cholesterol, and prevent cardiovascular diseases.

If you have any gut issues, like irritable bowel syndrome, take probiotics in small amounts to start, and gauge your body's reaction before continuing or increasing your intake.

- Oats and Bran

Oats and bran are filling, containing nearly all the nutrients necessary for health. The high amounts of soluble fiber slow digestion and promote the slow absorption of carbohydrates into the digestive system. So, these are great to include in a diet to stabilize your blood sugar.

- Seeds and Nuts

Nuts and seeds are rich in vitamin E, magnesium, zinc, and calcium. Magnesium plays an important role in blood sugar regulation. Also, flax seeds, chia, nuts, and nut butter are filling as they contain healthy fats to curb those in-between hunger pangs and regulate your blood sugar naturally. Peanut butter is not recommended because of possible high levels of trans fats and omega-6 fats, which are inflammatory. Try almond butter or pumpkin seed butter as an alternative.

- Legumes

Beans, chickpeas, and lentils contain magnesium that helps with blood sugar regulation. The fiber and protein in legumes also slow digestion and prevent sudden sugar spikes after a meal.

- Seafood

Fish and shellfish provide healthy fats, protein, vitamins, minerals, and antioxidants, all nutrients that help keep blood sugar levels stable. Protein is filling and thus prevents the quick release of glucose that causes those post-meal spikes. Furthermore, protein fills and stops you from feeling hungry and snacking on unhealthy, high carbohydrate foods.

Regularly eating oily fish like salmon, sardines, and mackerel containing healthy fats, is important for healthy brain function; they also support balanced blood sugar over the day.

Quick Reminder

- Body positivity means accepting your body with flaws and imperfections.
- Exercise helps lower stress levels because the brain releases feel-good hormones.
- Exercise for better mental health; feeling better about your appearance is a bonus.
- Long-term blood sugar imbalances can lead to type 2 diabetes and contribute to day-to-day slumps, irritation, and poor concentration.
- Diet, drinking enough water, proper sleep, and exercise lower blood sugar levels.
- A fiber-rich diet slows down the digestive process and glucose release, preventing blood sugar spikes.

5

Grounding Yourself

You are not separate from the whole. You are one with the sun, the earth, the air. You don't have a life. You are life.

Eckhart Tolle

JANET and I often arrived at work simultaneously and shared an elevator to our respective offices while chatting about the nasty weather, the terrible traffic, and our cats. One morning, she rushed into my office with chest pain, shortness of breath, sweating, and a racing heart. I saw the fear in her eyes while I helped her sit so I could assess her.

I had good news for Janet. She did not have a heart attack. She had experienced a panic or anxiety attack. Then followed a wake-up call; although Janet's life was not in immediate danger, prolonged and unchecked stress was now catching up with her and affecting her physical health. We had several conversations after this episode about relaxation techniques and time management to stop life from getting on top of her.

Janet was at a crossroads in her life. She listened to her body's wake-up call and made some changes to her lifestyle.

We lost contact after she changed jobs, but I recently ran into Janet at a coffee shop. I smiled when she mentioned that she uses a conscious breathing technique whenever possible.

Relaxation and Stress – The Full Story

How do you relax after a stressful day? Kick off your shoes and watch TV? Go to the pub with friends for a drink or two? Read a book? Play a few games of squash? Of course, there is nothing wrong with any of the above. They are all helpful in releasing stress and immediately feeling better.

On the surface, you relax while doing a relaxing activity. Why, then, are you still craving sugar? Why do you still drive yourself crazy by overthinking things at night while trying to get to sleep? Why do you still have panic attacks?

The answer is simple: Your body also needs deep rest to heal and relieve your anxiety. Short-term relaxing activities help you temporarily forget your difficulties. Of course, you can continue finding pleasure in healthy relaxation. However, your body also needs profound rest, where the heart rate and blood pressure drop. The body can rest entirely and move into the parasympathetic state of "Rest, Digest, Heal."

Given our busy days and stress levels, most of us struggle to reach this ideal state of deep rest.

Without breath, we all know that physical life is not possible. Still, breath also has spiritual meaning for people across many religions and movements:

- In the Quran, the breath relates to humans' physical and spiritual lives.
- Judaism and Christianity equate breath with God's spirit, thus central to their faiths.

- Your breath is your anchor; your anchor is your breath, is a well-used Buddhist chant.
- Yoga associates breath with life force energy known as prana and yoga practices are built around breathing.
- Martial art disciplines simultaneously use the breath to relax, focus, and be alert.

Why Use Breathing Exercises?

Your breath connects you to every body part: cells, muscles, brain, and organs. Your breath contributes to body awareness and your immediate surroundings. Conscious breathing grounds you physically, and because the physical body and mental and emotional processes are so intertwined, your breath is your anchor in acute stress.

Conscious, gentle breathing through the nose delivers more oxygen to stressed body cells. When stressed cells receive fresh oxygen through deep breathing, they immediately function more efficiently. It relieves the heart's workload, and the heart rate gradually slows.

As the body gradually relaxes, the respiratory system and heart slow down as the body needs less oxygen in a relaxed state. The parasympathetic nervous system ("rest, digest, heal") registers that the danger has passed, and the body and brain relax. In a relaxed state, the brain releases fewer stress hormones. Consequently, the body moves from fight-or-flight mode to a resting state. Feelings of stress and anxiety subside, and deep rest sets in.

There are many ways to practice breathing: mindful breathing, meditation, chanting, or praying. I recommend that you find a technique that suits your personality and lifestyle. Follow Janet's example and use the conscious connected breath technique regularly. Make it your personal anchor to prevent stress from overwhelming you, and notice if you're holding your breath.

Remember, an anxiety attack can hit anytime: while driving, during your commute, behind your desk, or in a meeting. Be prepared if it happens in public by exploring the techniques below as tools to help you in those disturbing moments. Breathing techniques are a life-saver during those awkward moments when the day seems to crush in on you.

This chapter offers help for those sudden panicky moments, and provides effective breathing techniques. Both have a place in your quest to alleviate stress, but I recommend that you familiarize yourself with deep breathing in the privacy of your home first.

Breathing Exercises

Deep breathing goes by many names: diaphragmatic, belly, and abdominal. Deep breathing guides the body and, eventually, the mind into a calmer rhythm. If practiced regularly, it can change your relationship with anxiety and stress. Psychologists recommend daily practicing deep breathing as it prevents and resolves anxious states. A regular session of 20 to 30 minutes will significantly relieve persistent anxiety (*Take a Deep Breath*, 2012).

Before you start deep breathing, notice how you and the people around you breathe. We usually breathe short and shallowly into our lungs in the chest area and often have long pauses between breaths. It adds to stress and tightness in the chest.

What happens in the body during deep breathing?

When you inhale deeply, you activate the diaphragm, the muscle between the heart and the lungs. As you inhale, the diaphragm contracts and moves downward. The extra space allows the lungs to expand. Deep inhaling sends the breath through the airways and fills the lung bases, taking in more oxygen-rich air. The belly rises, and the cells of the body receive oxygen. Once the body is refreshed, the breath naturally slows down, causing calmness and deep relaxation.

This type of breathing helps because as you exhale, the diaphragm returns to its former position and presses stale air with carbon dioxide out through the airways.

How to Practice Deep Breathing

Yoga, meditation, mindfulness, and many other practices incorporate deep breathing, but the beauty of deep breathing is that you can practice it anywhere you feel comfortable.

- Start in a comfortable position sitting with your back and neck supported or lying on your bed or the floor.
- Breathe in through the nose and out through the nose.
- Place one hand on your chest and the other on the belly.
- Inhale again until you can feel how your belly expands and lifts your hand.
- Exhale and feel how your belly drops from your hand.
- Repeat this while concentrating on your belly movement.

When you are restless, your thoughts may wander, and you lose concentration. Focus intensely on your body's sensations when your cells are fed with life-giving oxygen. Experience every part of your body drinking in your practice, and use this to guide your breathing rhythm. There are no hard and fast rules. The purpose is to help you focus. Continue deep breathing for at least ten minutes to allow your body to move into a deep and relaxing state.

Conscious Connected Breathing

Leonard Orr introduced this breathing technique in the 1970s, and it has since gained popularity among therapists and psychologists. The key to conscious connected (also called conscious continuous) breathing is inhaling and exhaling without pausing. Leonard Orr advocated that conscious connected breathing could reduce stress and tension because continuously connecting inhaling and exhaling causes physiological changes (Wheble, n.d.). These shifts in the body enhance self-awareness, awareness of your surroundings, and of others. Thus, the physiological impact of this breathing technique results in increased emotional awareness and allows for personal growth.

Conscious connected breathing includes sound, working with the body, and water, and relies strongly on affirmation techniques. Professionals from various schools of thought use this breathing technique in psychotherapeutic therapy; consequently, the details might differ. However, most professionals believe it helps with physical, mental, and spiritual healing.

The core components are:

- There are no pauses between inhales and exhales.
- It activates the diaphragm to breathe into the belly, the sides, front, and back, tops of the lungs, expanding in all six directions equally without tension or tightness.
- Imagining the lungs as balloons can be helpful; think of expanding to 60-70% of your lung's capacity, so the breath is comfortable and feels gentle and natural.
- The exhale is passive; let go of your breath.
- Breathe in and out through the nose (this way there is no concern about hyperventilating).

Box Breathing

Box breathing is a popular technique to capture one's focus. The mind concentrates on counting; consequently, it does not wander so easily. Box or square breathing has four stages, like the four sides of a box or a square.

- Sit or lie comfortably as you would prepare for deep breathing. Inhale and exhale a few times deeply.
- Breathe in, counting to four in your head.
- Hold your breath, counting to four.
- Exhale, counting to four.
- Count to four on a full exhalation, then inhale again to a count of four.

Box breathing is great to use before a presentation or a meeting, it brings in a strong sense of relaxation by bringing in the parasympathetic nervous system to rest, digest and heal.

4-7-8 Breathing

This focused breathing technique is widespread, and can be done whenever you have a moment to sit or lie comfortably. Feel free to change the duration of each step as you find comfortable. However, it's best to keep the ratio: short inhale, holding the breath somewhat longer, and exhaling even longer.

- Start in the same position as you would with all deep breathing techniques by sitting or lying comfortably with a straight spine.
- Place the tip of the tongue behind the top front teeth.
- Exhale fully to empty your lungs completely.
- Inhale, counting slowly to four.
- Hold your breath, counting slowly to seven.
- Exhale, counting slowly to eight.

Experts recommend that beginners repeat this four times twice a day. You will begin to see results after a few days. Over time, your body will naturally fall into this rhythm, and you will find your sleep easier.

Lion's Breath

This technique is used in yoga and Qigong and can initially seem slightly unusual. Exhale through the mouth, stick the tongue out, and roar like a lion. Strange though it might seem, it is an enjoyable way to eliminate stress. If you are uncomfortable at first, give it a chance. It is quite fun, and allows you to let go of tension in an amusing way.

Lion's breath stimulates the throat chakra related to communication, refined creativity, and self-expression, thus using the vocal cords and lungs.

- You have a few options for starting lion breath: sitting, on your knees in hero pose, or on all fours.
- Focus on something ahead of you or gaze inward, concentrating on the third eye.
- If sitting, lean slightly forward and grab hold of your knees. If on all fours, ground yourself securely by gripping the floor with your hands and resting firmly on the top of your feet.
- Inhale through your mouth.
- With your wide-open mouth, stick your tongue out and down toward your chin.
- Exhale deeply, forcing the breath across your tongue while making a "Haa"-sound. Do this forcefully for maximum effect.
- Visualize the negativity inside you as something physical—a murky cloud or a dark object—moving with your breath out of your body.
- Breathe normally for a few cycles before repeating the lion's breath.

Grounding Techniques

Unfortunately, traumatic experiences can stay with us for a long time. The trauma might be over, but the body and brain still carry the memories and pain. Typical symptoms are shortness of breath, a racing heart, sleeplessness, memory loss, crying, angry outbursts, and feeling emotionally drained and numb.

In trauma response, your body releases high amounts of adrenaline and stress chemicals, and the events tend to be stored deeply. Your memories are often so intense that your brain temporarily does not allow positive cognitive processes, such as pleasant thoughts and memories, to surface.

Psychologists and therapists use grounding techniques to help people recover from severe trauma and stress. When you ground yourself in the here and now, your memories and thought patterns

turn away from the unpleasant experience to focus on your immediate surroundings. And, creating space and distance brings relief.

Grounding techniques are actions that distract you from disturbing
thoughts and emotions. Try various techniques; some might work
better in a specific situation.

Grounding Chair

This grounding practice might seem deceptively simple, but it is a
good starting point to remind you of your foundations, physically
and emotionally. You can do this anywhere—at home, the office, a
restaurant, and even commuting.

- Sit in a comfortable chair with your feet on the floor.
- Close your eyes and focus on your breath. Inhale slowly,
  counting to three, and exhale slowly.
- Now, bring your awareness into your body. Move around
  on the seat and settle in supporting your back.
- Note the feeling of the contact points between you and the
  seat.
- Move your focus to your feet: Press them firmly into the
  floor and note how it feels.
- Next, move your focus to your head. Feel the energy of
  your thoughts moving down your body; be aware of the
  flow through your neck, chest, abdomen, pelvis, legs, feet,
  and into the ground. If you struggle with this concept,
  imagine this moving energy as a moving, comforting light
  or color.
- As the energy flows out of your head and body, feel how
  your physical body becomes more relaxed, and allow the
  energy to exit your body through the soles of your feet.
  Surrender this energy to the earth.
- Feel the lingering calm in your body when the energy flows
  into the floor.

Grounding Technique: 5-4-3-2-1

- Name five things you see. Try to skip the more obvious things like a house or a tree and think of smaller details: the pattern on tree bark, or the color variations of your dog's coat.
- Name four things you can touch. Again, concentrate on the subtle nuances: the feeling of the paper of a glossy magazine or the gravel's roughness. Try to find a variety of textures: soft, wet, hot, cold.
- Name three things you can hear, concentrating on the white noise your mind usually cuts out: the fridge's humming or the wind through the leaves.
- Name two things you can smell, like the neighbor's curry or the musty smell of wet leaves.
- Name one thing you can taste. Take a mint or a fruit and describe the different sensations—sour, sweet, bitter, cold.

Name Items in Different Categories

This technique might remind you of the childhood games you played on a road trip with the family. You can adapt this technique to suit you. It not only tests your general knowledge and forces your mind to move away from your lingering worries, but it also reminds you that the world is not all bad. There are still good things.

- Write down several categories, such as animals, singers, and cities. The possibilities are endless, and you can make up your own categories.
- List as many things under each category as you can remember, and challenge yourself to order them. For example, list all the names of the cities you've visited in the last year.

Practical Anxiety Relief Techniques "On-the-Go"

Anxiety or panic attacks can happen unexpectedly and in the most inconvenient places. For these moments, a practical toolkit of mental exercises to do subtly and unobtrusively in public is very effective. The idea is that you challenge yourself to describe a process or a thing, and in doing so, get some distance from the disturbing thoughts or images in your mind.

- Count backward.
- Say the alphabet backward.
- Spell names backward.
- Read a billboard backward.
- Describe an object in your immediate environment: a bus, a tree, or a shopfront.
- Draw the object in your mind.
- Think of the names of your family members, list them from the oldest to youngest, and add each of their birthdays.
- Describe the steps of an activity, such as cooking a favorite dish.

Quick Reminder

- Breathing exercises are your anchor in managing stress, anxiety, and panic attacks.
- Deep abdominal breathing slows down involuntary functions such as heart rate, blood pressure, and oxygen supply to the body and brain cells, which brings about deep rest and natural self-healing.
- Daily deep breathing sessions are best to prevent anxiety and panic attacks.
- There are several breathing techniques to practice in private and public, which help to lower stress levels.
- After a traumatic event, memories are often so intense that the brain temporarily blocks positive thoughts and feelings.

- Grounding techniques are actions that bring you into the present moment. Try various techniques; some might work better in a specific situation.
- Grounding techniques are handy tools to address anxiety attacks as and when they happen.

6

Be The Light That You Are

 "Caring for someone with anxiety is not about fixing them, it's about supporting them. Offer them a safe space to express themselves, and remind them of their own inner strength."

Jack Kornfield

EVERYONE LOVES you when you're upbeat and happy and laughing — of course, being in a carefree state all the time is easier said than done, especially when you struggle with anxiety, panic, or stress.

If you are juggling your job, family, parenthood, caring roles, and community commitments, it can feel like you don't have time to explain; you don't want to be seen as not being able to handle it or somehow "weak." So you push yourself on, often not resting or sleeping because the lists of "to do's" are running through your mind as well as all the things that could go wrong with those tasks, plus worrying that you're not sleeping, leading to more lost sleep! Many people think anxiety is just overthinking, but at its extreme, it can make you feel numb, frozen, and crushed by the weight of your commitments.

Christine's Conundrum

Imagine the case of Christine, a bright, sassy 30-something, married mother of 2 teenagers working in education. Her favorite band was due to play in the city at the weekend after she came to see me for an appointment. I knew Christine as a very capable, if a somewhat anxious woman. However, on this particular day, she looked tired and harassed, we were talking about her insomnia when she burst into tears and told me she just couldn't bear to attend the Coldplay concert at the weekend and that she was so upset with herself and her anxiety, but she simply couldn't do the things she loved anymore saying, *"I'm turning into someone I don't recognize!"*.

Her partner had bought the concert tickets six months before as a surprise birthday gift and at the time she was overjoyed, but now the concert was only days away, Christine felt she simply couldn't face the journey into the city, the bustle of the crowds on the train, and the doubtless late night. She was stuck overthinking all the possible bad things that could happen. Interestingly, she was completely aware that she was catastrophizing, so she was simultaneously beating herself up for it!

Christine was decided, she was going to wipe her tears away and pluck up the courage to tell her partner that they simply couldn't go because it would *"all just be too much!"*

That's what anxiety can do.

It can stop you from doing the things you most enjoy in life and leave you feeling flat, exhausted, and disappointed with yourself.

I spoke with Christine gently about the situation, and we talked about all the wonderful things she loved about the band, their last album, and how the stage show was so impressive when she'd seen them a few years before. I could see how torn she was, really wanting to want to go to the concert, but knowing her fear and doubt were all that was holding her back, as we spoke and as I prompted her, she started to question her automatic negative thoughts (ANTs).

We talked practically, how could she structure her day if she did attend the show so she had plenty of time and there was no feeling of rushing to get into the venue on time? We discussed on-the-spot breathing techniques to use in case of panic and the unbroken hours of nourishing sleep that had been eluding her for some time.

By the time she left, she was daring to feel hope; for her, sleep was vital, and with a few more hours over the nights ahead and a planned taxi ride into the city and back (not the train!), Christine and her partner went to the concert. A few weeks later, she reported that she managed to fend off panic with sleep and good planning and, overall, had allowed herself to let her hair down and feel more carefree than she had in a long time.

Making a Difference

If you want to make a difference in the life of someone who has anxiety, one of the most valuable gifts you can share with them is information.

Throughout this book, I share simple, practical, holistic ways to Self-Heal Anxiety. Each of us can connect deeply to our inner world, accept ourselves and our past, and ultimately discover unshakeable love for ourselves. If that feels far off right now, the techniques shared in this book walk you through the process step-by-step so that you can overcome obstacles that may stand in your way.

By feeling your emotions, bringing awareness to your behaviors, and using the tools I'm sharing, you can make significant strides in your healing and curb anxiety before it takes over your peace of mind.

Thankfully, we live in a time when discussing anxiety is increasingly commonplace. Famous names like Adele and Emma Stone have all spoken candidly about their battles with anxiety and panic. Lady Gaga, meanwhile, has openly talked about how pushing yourself too far mentally, physically, and emotionally leads to burnout and exhaustion, and it can take a long time to recover.

Now, you might not have the eyes of the world's media on you, but you can let others know that sitting back and allowing anxiety to take over is not their only option.

By leaving a review of this book on Amazon or GoodReads, you can motivate others to make the best use of their precious time, treat their bodies with love and kindness, and learn the simple, practical techniques that keep anxiety attacks and sleepless nights at bay. This way, more and more women can develop strengths that will empower them to become resilient against anxiety.

With just a few words, you can be the light someone needs to pull themselves out of a hole; out of feeling stuck with the walls closing in, barely able to take a breath, an overwhelming state we can reach when we have been running on empty for far too long.

Scan The QR Code To Leave Your Review On Amazon Today

PART II

Embracing Wholeness

7

Releasing Tension

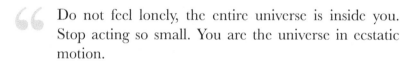

> Do not feel lonely, the entire universe is inside you. Stop acting so small. You are the universe in ecstatic motion.

Rumi

IN THIS PART of the book, you will find several additional practices to add to the skills learned in the book's first half. The methods in the following chapters are tools to strengthen the positive steps you have taken thus far to lower your stress levels. Stress is part and parcel of life, and it will help to have a set of tools ready to prevent daily stress from building up into full-blown anxiety attacks.

<u>Danni's Story</u>

Danni's life changed the night she walked home from the pub and took a shortcut across the park to her apartment. She told no one what happened and went to work the next day and the next. The days became weeks, and the weeks became months. She increasingly isolated herself by staying at her desk during lunch. One day, a colleague returned for her phone and tapped Danni lightly on the shoulder.

Danni started screaming and ended up in my office, shivering and whimpering. It took a while before I got to the bottom of her anxiety and insomnia. Danni was exhausted, bottling her emotions up and not sleeping. Night after night, she tossed and turned, her heart racing. I introduced her to progressive muscle relaxation, which helped her release the tension in her body, and her sleep eventually improved.

But Danni had a long road ahead. Read in the next chapter more about Danni's determination not to let the trauma and the consequential anxiety take over her life.

Progressive Muscle Relaxation

Dr. Edmund Jacobson formulated this method a century ago (Toussaint, 2021). He believed that by concentrating on contracting and relaxing your muscles in a specific order, the mind instinctively follows for total physical and mental relaxation. The key to this method is to contract and relax one muscle group after another.

Experts believe progressive muscle relaxation has several other benefits besides anxiety relief. It improves sleep, helps with neck and lower back pain, and reduces migraines and blood pressure. Professional singers and public speakers often use a more localized form of this technique to stimulate the vocal cords.

You will tense and relax your muscles group by group from the feet upward for 20 to 30 seconds at a time. Concentrate on a specific body part by imagining your entire body's tension shifting there. This shifting tensing, and relaxing is the foundation of the progressive muscle relaxation technique. Repeat this according to the following guidance.

- Stand comfortably with your arms by your sides.

- Move your focus to your breath. Rhythmically, deeply inhale through the nose and slowly exhale through the mouth for about two minutes. Do not rush this introductory phase; settle into the rhythm and relax.
- Now, move your focus down to your feet, and picture all the tension in your body, concentrating on your feet. Keep the tension for 20 to 30 seconds, repeating a mantra to help you hold on to the tension. Choose a phrase to go with the action, such as, "My day's stress has settled in my feet; they are tense and tight." Use your own words; this practice is intensely personal, and the words should come from your heart and mind.
- Slowly release the tension. Relax the muscles gradually for 20 to 30 seconds. Again, your mantra should be a guide to slowly relaxing the muscles; thus, speak from your deepest self. Repeat: "Holding on to stress is senseless; I now let the stress leave my feet and allow room for relaxing calm."
- When you have done these two steps, move your focus to your thighs and consciously tense your thigh muscles while slowly repeating the mantra of your choice. Then, gradually release the tension while repeating your chosen phrase.
- Go through the entire body, tensing and relaxing one muscle group after the other, all the time matching your mantra to your action: core muscles, chest, hands, arms, shoulders, and neck. (The shoulders and neck are notorious for holding tension without us even realizing it.) Slowly tense your shoulders; pull your shoulders up to your ears and hold. Not only do the shoulders move physically, but the tension also spills over into your neck area. Release equally slowly while repeating your mantra.
- Give special attention to your face. It's important not to rush through your facial muscles. Stress often causes headaches, as we tend to keep a lot of tension in our heads, especially in the area between the brows. Give yourself the

time and space to acknowledge your stress and its effect on your body.

- With time, you might feel the tension flowing out of your body. Acknowledge it by repeating to yourself something like, "My body and mind are now relaxed. I am grateful to be able to rest." Remember, your relief experience is unique; express your feelings in your own words.

If you struggle to sleep, you can repeat this technique lying down.

Physical Coping Methods to Combat Anxiety

You have come a long way reading this book and learning about and practicing various techniques to combat anxiety. Still, an unexpected anxiety attack can suddenly grip you and leave you paralyzed with fear. In those moments, you need something to immediately release physical stress and signal the brain to release feel-good hormones.

The following methods will help you when panic overwhelms you. Try them and see how relief sets in.

Shake It Off

Do as the popular song tells us: shake it off. Stand up and shake your hands and arms vigorously. Alternatively, sit on the edge of a chair and firmly hold on as you actively shake your legs. The intense movement, although in only one body part, releases tension and gives you a mental break from panic and anxiety by bringing your attention to the body.

Fidget It Away

Fidget toys are not for children only. Fidgeting often evokes annoyance from onlookers, but those small, restless movements often help a stressed person to cope. Fidgeting helps improve focus, especially for people with attention deficit disorder.

These toys work because they allow focus while turning the volume down on intrusive thoughts. By keeping your hands busy, your mind 'forgets' and temporarily lets go of the negative emotions. Get yourself a fidget toy: a spinner, stress ball, or a fidget cube.

Play Finger Games

Use your thumb to tap the other fingers one by one while spelling out a soothing word or phrase. It's a double whammy—the tapping distracts your mind from your anxious thoughts. Also, spelling a reassuring message enhances the words' meaning and brings you comfort.

Get Sour

A strong sensory experience, such as extreme sourness or bitterness, shocks the body and distracts the mind. Your taste buds and salivary glands go into overdrive, producing spit and trying to neutralize the taste. It helps to get some distance from a feeling of panic and allows you time to ground yourself by concentrating on the sensation in your mouth.

Go For Cold

Ice baths are gaining popularity, especially for athletes after a hard workout. We use an ice pack for sprains and swollen joints to reduce inflammation. Ice soothes the muscles and stimulates deep breathing, which calms the body. The sudden cold also brings emotional relief.

If submerging your face in ice-cold water does not sound possible to you, lie on a cold bathroom floor. The extreme cold alerts the parasympathetic nervous system, and it messages the body to relax. The solidity of the floor provides a sense of stability.

Knock on Heaven's Door

This exercise is fun, and is a favorite technique in yoga and Qigong. You stand straight with knees slightly bent and relaxed with your feet about hip-width apart. Hang your arms loosely at your sides. Now, start swinging your arms from one side to the other, gently twisting at the hips. You may feel like gently pivoting each foot with the swing. Closing the hands into loose fists, gently tap the body at the level of the kidneys. In Qigong, this is said to help dispel fear. The movement helps you forget your disturbing thoughts, and patting the sides of the body distracts your attention even more.

Prepare yourself for emergency self-help. Try these techniques; change or adapt them as part of your toolkit to proactively combat your anxiety. You take precautions with your physical health by taking supplements or watching your sugar intake; do the same with your anxiety.

Aromatherapy: Finding Your Inner Calm

Essential oil or aromatherapy uses plant extracts as a sensory treatment for anxiety and stress relief. The practice is centuries old and has gained global popularity over the last few decades. Doctors and therapists increasingly use aromatherapy as part of a holistic approach to health. The pleasant scents stimulate the amygdala, a part of the brain involved in our emotions.

Aromatherapy involves more than lovely scents that evoke pleasant emotional reactions. Essential oils have several other benefits. Some are antimicrobial to help to guard against infections and have antibiotic, antiviral, antifungal, or antiparasitic qualities.

Children, pregnant women, older people, and people with serious health issues should seek professional advice before using essential oils.

Topical Oils

Essential oils are concentrated and are thus very strong. Undiluted oil can burn the skin; therefore, in topical oils, the extract is mixed with carrier oils such as sweet almond or olive oil.

Do an allergy test to ensure the oil or cream is not too strong. Dilute a few drops of essential oil into a carrier oil like sesame oil, almond oil, or jojoba. Rub it onto a small area of the soft skin of your forearm. Wait for at least 24 hours before using more of the product.

<u>Inhaling Oils</u>

Essential oils are concentrated extracts, and a few drops in a bath are sufficient. You can also use a diffuser. Oils have several medicinal properties. An oil like mint or eucalyptus can decongest the airways and relieve sinus infections, colds. The pleasant scents stimulate the brain to release feel-good hormones, which contribute to mental and physical health.

Essential Oils for Anxiety Relief

Here is a selection of essential oils known to be beneficial in Anxiety.

You can inhale calming essential oils sprinkled on a handkerchief or dilute the essential oil in a carrier oil and apply it to the pulse points on your wrists or sides of the neck. Another option is to add your chosen scent mixture to the palms of your hands, then cup your hands together and inhale deeply. To get a longer-lasting effect, you may want to use an essential oil diffuser in your office or bedroom.

<u>Lavender</u> is a favorite in many gardens, and can be used for anxiety, relaxing muscles, and fighting inflammation. Some surgeons use it to calm patients before surgery, and a study at the University of Minnesota found that lavender may improve sleep (Brazier, 2017). Its floral scent with herbal undertones make it globally popular.

<u>Bergamot</u> is from the citrus family and is reduced from the orange's rind. Tests on rats showed that it helps with anxiety when inhaled (Nall, 2017). It also can lift depression symptoms.

<u>Clary sage</u> comes from the south of Europe. The herb, with its large leaves and small bluish-white flowers, grows quite tall. Both leaves and flowers are distilled for oil. Clary sage has several medicinal properties, such as lowering blood pressure, and helping relieve urinary tract infections and incontinence.

Lemon oil is well-known and widely used in most cultures for its refreshing citrus scent. Be careful when out in the sun, though. Lemon essential oil increases the chance of getting sunburn and aggravates the conditions of existing sunburn.

Ylang-ylang oil is reduced from the *Canaga ordorata* tree's lovely yellow flowers. This tropical tree is native to the East, but has spread globally. It soothes the skin and calms the nervous system.

Holy basil oil is one of three types of basil oils. It has ancient roots, and its Sanskrit name is *Tulsi,* which means incomparable. Prayer beads often contain holy basil stalks. Holy basil can irritate the skin; use it with care. Its warm scent calms the nerves. It also helps with migraines, headaches, fatigue, blood pressure, anxiety and depression.

Neroli (Orange blossom) oil comes from the bitter orange tree's flowers. Its scent is well-loved and sweet with spicy undertones. It relieves stress, improves insomnia, and stabilizes blood pressure and estrogen levels.

Rose (Damask) oil comes from one of the oldest roses in history. Historians believe the rose originates from Damascus, but has since spread worldwide. Damask roses symbolize love. No wonder it is a stalwart in perfume making, as it gives a feeling of contentment and improves anxiety and stress.

Chamomile is a herb with small daisy-like flowers. The oil comes from the flowers and has a subtle scent that makes it tolerable even for people who suffer from hay fever. Some doctors use it to calm patients during complex medical treatments.

Valerian oil is from a tall grassland plant from the valerian family. *Valerian Officinalis* oil helps people to fall asleep quicker. However, check the source before buying, as some inferior products are sold as valerian oil.

Peppermint leaves were used by the Romans for crowns and sprays and as table decorations on special occasions. The oil comes from the flowers of the peppermint plant, and its scent is cooling and refreshing. It calms the mind and is effective to use when anxious.

Frankincense oil is as old as written history, and comes from the resin of the Boswellia tree, indigenous to the Middle East, Somalia, and Pakistan. Christians believe frankincense was one of the three gifts the magi from the East gave the baby Jesus.

It helps with stress by reducing the heart rate and lowering blood pressure. It contains two acetates (chemical compounds) that induce calmness.

Quick Reminder

- If you struggle to relax, try progressive muscle relaxation.
- Progressive muscle relaxation is contracting and releasing one muscle group at a time.
- Aromatherapy has been used for many centuries in holistic health care. It uses plant extracts (essential oils) to inhale or to apply topically.
- Use your essential oil with a carrier oil, on a handkerchief, on your pulse points, or in a diffuser to utilize their anxiety-relieving properties.
- Use essential oils with care, as they are highly concentrated extracts.

Let Your Negative Thoughts Go

 Inner peace begins the moment you choose not to allow another person or event to control your emotions.

Pema Chödrön

AN INNOCENT BUT unexpected tap on her shoulder alerted Danni to how deeply traumatized she was. She had stopped wearing makeup and was now dressed in baggy clothes. She had not been to a movie in months, and declined all invitations to socialize with her friends and colleagues. Her mind was constantly abuzz with negative thoughts about herself. Shame, hurt, anxiety, and fear mingled into a heavy burden weighing her down.

She started remembering snatches of conversations with her mother reprimanding her about too-short skirts, too-bright lipstick, and staying out too late. She recalled her college friends' teasing about her outfits. She decided the dress she wore that night was too revealing. In Danni's mind, innocent remarks and playful teasing morphed into guilt, blame, rejection, and shame.

This chapter gives insight into the distortions our minds sometimes fabricate, and how to recognize this to break the cycle of negative thought patterns.

Challenge Negative Thinking

Are you constantly thinking negatively about yourself? Do you tend to relive unpleasant conversations and events that strengthen your negative thought patterns? Please note: You are not the only one playing negative mental loops on repeat. Automatic negative thoughts (ANTs) plague all of us. As the name indicates, they pop up automatically and challenge our emotional well-being.

Examples of ANTs are:

"I can't"

"It just won't work for me"

"I'm not good enough"

"This won't end well"

Often, we harbor these background thought loops for many years, and they become cemented into our psyches as facts or truths. We lose perspective and see them as reality.

It helps to discuss these with a therapist, a trusted friend, or a family member. Take their advice and perspective seriously, and write it down. Remember, these thoughts are so ingrained in your mind that they have become a habit. Later in the chapter, you can find ways to replace them with more realistic and positive perspectives.

Negative Thinking Styles

Below is a discussion of several negative thinking styles. Study these and note which ones you are prone to have. It will help if you know it is normal and there are methods to stop these disturbing thought processes. They happen to all of us, not only those who experienced severe traumas like Danni.

Catastrophizing sprouts from life's fickleness: You worry about job security, your husband's health, your son's behavior, and the country's dire state. Some psychologists call this the worry spiral because your worries spiral out of control and take over your life.

You expect the worst to happen, and these fears are real to you. Cognitive behavioral therapy (CBT) can help you in person or even using online programs.

Overgeneralization is when you see one incident and decide it applies to a wider situation. You see a young man misbehaving and decide all young men are criminals.

Check-in with yourself: If you are late for work once, should your boss hold back your promotion because you are unreliable? Similarly, if you tend to overgeneralize, listen with an open heart and give someone a second chance before you pass hasty judgment. There is truth in the saying: Do to others as you would have them do to you.

Personalization happens when you take something unrelated to you personally. If you have high levels of stress and anxiety, you might believe your colleagues exclude you intentionally from a meeting. Or think a remark in passing about an unflattering hairstyle referred to you. Your anxiety contributes to your hypersensitivity.

Polarized thinking is when you tend to consider things in their most extreme form. You are never neutral about anything and presume the same about others. You think of yourself as someone who knows her mind. You are either for or against a person, an issue, or a happening. You like someone or something, or you don't. Your colleague is either for you or against you.

Usually, the truth is somewhere in-between, and someone can like you but differ on a specific matter. Your anxiety affects your ability to judge each situation on merit and see the bigger picture.

Mind reading happens often. You think you know what someone is thinking by merely observing the person's facial expressions or lack of a show of emotion. You decide that someone does not agree with you or does not like you by looking at them. You ignore the possibility that the person was not thinking about you at all at that moment.

Mental filtering means you have a predisposed negative opinion of something, someone, or even yourself. You filter out anything to the contrary, and only notice things that support your negative thoughts. You don't see anything positive, and ignore positive feedback. This filtering contributes to stress and anxiety, and can jeopardize your well-being.

Discounting the positive is closely connected to mental filtering. This negative thinking discredits any positivity that might question your negative thoughts. By destroying any positive evidence, you strengthen your negative beliefs. Psychologists describe this as a learned skill to boost your negativity.

"Should or ought to" thoughts are often based on cultural and social perceptions of how one should or ought to behave. You are schooled to think that things must only be done in a certain way, and question anything that does not support your ideas or worldview.

Labeling ignores the multi-layered and multi-dimensional nature of being human. Tagging yourself or someone else with a single negative description, such as lazy, stupid, or incapable, disregards the many qualities present. When labeling, you unfairly criticize yourself or someone else, leading to misunderstandings that carry forward and underlie future interactions or attitudes with future tasks.

How to Stop Negative Thinking

Cognitive behavioral therapy works on the principle that restructuring our thinking can significantly improve anxiety disorders. A cognitive behavioral therapist or online program helps you to identify hot thoughts, that recurring false thinking that causes misconceptions and unhappiness.

You can also do a lot to help yourself combat negative thought patterns and simultaneously lessen your anxiety. Keep in mind, these negative patterns have been established over a long period. They will not disappear within a week or two. But with consistent work and the techniques here, you can overcome constant negative thought loops and discover a different, more uplifting way to approach life.

One technique is to use journaling to help you. Carve out some time to sit down with a pen and paper, identify your thoughts, and write them down. As you continue to write, you may discover more about the origins of your thoughts and what caused them. If you—with the help of a therapist or on your own—can recognize your habitual negative thinking, you have reached an important milestone. You identified them, whether they are remnants from your childhood or were caused by a specific incident.

You are now ready to reconstruct those negative thoughts into positive ones. The next step is to place each aspect under the spotlight and test it against reality.

Danni found that she reverted to negative thinking patterns in social situations. She wanted to relax with friends, but was terrified that she might send out the wrong vibes by how she dressed, laughed, and even walked. She made this connection at her company's year-end function. She needed to go to the restroom, but didn't want to walk to the ladies' room because she feared she would attract the wrong kind of attention as she passed through the bar.

Danni worked with her therapist to understand that the assault she went through had little to do with sexual attraction, but with the actions of a disturbed person using violence to control women.

Danni learned to monitor her assumptions and check them against the reality of the situation.

Mindfulness Versus Stopping Your Thoughts

Our thoughts determine how we act. If we are constantly depressed and anxious, these negative emotions become our behavior, and even part of our character.

Mindfulness is a practice where we distance ourselves from our thoughts and feelings and view them without judgment. Just notice your thoughts and how they make you feel. Don't try to avoid them.

It gives you a more objective insight into your mental state and helps you to see how your thoughts influence your personal and professional life. Mindfulness is a tool to recognize negative thought patterns and their adverse effects.

It is only natural to want to stop your negative thought processes as soon as they happen. Unfortunately, this is easier said than done. You might successfully suppress them sometimes, but they will pop up repeatedly. Below, you will find several techniques to replace negative thoughts with positive ones.

Positive Mantra: Use a positive mantra to rephrase the negative thought. Choose something meaningful. Try to attach your mantra to your negative thoughts, but reword it into a positive statement. Janet, who suffered anxiety attacks, adopted the well-known yoga mantra "My breath is my anchor; my anchor is my breath."

Take a Break from Work: Plan a break from work when you are overwhelmed. Be considerate and do your bit to make the project's deadline, but take a break once the project has been completed. Get some distance between you and the chaos and give yourself some perspective. And no, the office will not collapse without you. You have done your bit; now it's time to look after yourself.

Give Your Soul Some TLC: Take time to attend to your needs, whether it's giving yourself some space from work or family obligations. Like Lucia, learn to say no sometimes, and use your me-time to heal and rest. Set boundaries for yourself and stick to them. Don't be so hard on yourself and feel guilty if you put yourself first sometimes. Be gentle with yourself and give yourself permission to be the priority sometimes. As a human, you're entitled to your emotions and time to heal.

Don't Flee Those Feelings: Let your disappointment, grief, or anger out. Face your emotions and accept them as valid. If you are hurt or have strong feelings, they have to surface and be allowed. You won't get rid of them by ignoring them. Give them space and time; cry if you want, stomp and shout. You need time to work through your emotions. Authenticity is not always pretty, but it is always true.

Don't Wait for Justice to Prevail: The person who did you wrong may get away without ever apologizing. Don't allow anybody to have a hold on you. Martin Luther King Jr. summarized the danger of bearing a grudge when he said, "Because if you only have anger, the anger will paralyze you. You cannot do anything constructive." (Greenfieldboyce, 2019). Your happiness does not depend on their apology. Concentrate on the good things in your life. Focus on what you are grateful for, and let life take care of its injustices in its own time.

Your Community, Your World: None of us is an island, and in recent times we've experienced the damage that isolation can do. We all need to cry sometimes; when that time comes for you, let it be cleansing. Reach out to a trusted friend or a therapist. Choose someone with empathy who will listen without judgment. Be present with yourself. Understanding and verbalizing complex thoughts or feelings and allowing yourself to feel safe while being seen and heard can be deeply healing. Hopefully, your confidante is wise enough to accompany you out of the darkness when you are ready to move toward the light.

Quick Reminder

- Automatic negative thoughts (ANTs) are normal; we all have them from time to time.

- Cognitive behavioral therapy (CBT) is an effective practice to help you recognize and change negative thought patterns and improve your quality of life.
- Holding on to anger is bitter and poisonous and ultimately only hurts you. Use the techniques in this chapter to find a way to let go and leave justice up to the Universe.

9

Introducing Your Zen

 When you become comfortable with uncertainty, infinite possibilities open up in your life.

Eckhart Tolle

IMAGINE yourself calm while the clock to a deadline is ticking. Your computer just crashed; your boss wants the latest sales statistics *now*. The teacher calls; your son has a strange rash. You take a sip of water and text your husband to please get in touch with the teacher. You calmly ask your boss to let you access the report from his computer.

Zen is an attitude that helps you to adopt a peaceful lifestyle amidst the frantic rat race around you. Impossible, you say? Let's explore it further. Zen is about having insight, inner strength, and seeing things in perspective. You make more objective decisions if you see life's big and small challenges as part of the bigger picture. Zen teaches self-control, calming the mind, settling those ANTs so you can handle whatever flows your way.

When you develop your Zen mindset, you don't ignore a crisis. On the contrary; it enables you to function more effectively, because you do not allow stress or negative emotions to overwhelm your decisions and actions. With a calm mind, you can look at a situation without judgment, focus better, and find solutions quicker.

Finding your Zen helps you train your mind actively through meditation to know stillness and calm regularly.

Journaling To Find Your Center

Journaling is a great way to get perspective on your thoughts, fears, and dreams. Putting what is going on in your mind into words or colors and shapes gives them physical form. It helps to order your thoughts and see them more objectively, which helps to still any emotional disquiet.

How to Journal

- Keep it simple and do what works for you: pen and paper, laptop, or phone.
- Set a routine for journaling: daily, weekly, or monthly. The only prerequisite is sticking to your plan; this is the key.
- Write, draw, paint, or compose poems or songs to express yourself. Only you will see your journal; do what you like best.
- If you don't know what to write, start with what is going on in your mind right now: fears, anger, worries, or all of them. Remember, your journal is for your eyes only: let go and get creative!
- When you have finished for the day, read through it again and ask yourself a few questions:
- Are your fears realistic? Do you recognize any ANTs (automatic negative thoughts) described in the previous chapter?
- Is it likely that the dreaded event will happen?

- Are there any steps you can take to prevent it from happening?
- How can you lessen the impact or turn it to your advantage if it happens? Think about your strengths and the resources that could help you manage the crisis if it happens.

Use your strengths and resources to manage the situation if a crisis is inevitable.

Journaling can seem intimidating, however, once you get started and into a regular practice, it can be such a release. It's a really powerful tool for exploring your inner world and getting to know yourself better.

Journaling and then evaluating your thoughts and feelings is empowering. You can't always stop bad things from happening, but you can find creative solutions for how you will manage them. You can't control external factors, but you can resource yourself; use your imagination and skills so that you are ready to face all that life has in store for you.

Acceptance

Negative thoughts interplay with difficult emotions; one begets the other, and round we go. We can get stuck in a downward spiral at times. We might want to get rid of disturbing thoughts and emotions at all costs, plaster on a smile, and carry on. But as the saying goes, "You've got to feel it to heal it." Pushing down and suppressing emotions is such a strongly-conditioned response in so many that we often don't realize that stuffing a feeling down means that the energy of that emotion will leak out elsewhere, and usually when we least expect it.

If you wish to lessen the effect of thoughts and feelings on the quality of your relationships, work, and family life, finding a way to accept your thoughts and emotions without judgment will help you.

In psychology, acceptance is not resignation; instead, you acknowledge your emotions, but don't judge them or yourself. Importantly, taking a stance of presence, not attaching story, simply feeling and accepting. Delete this sentence: Building your self-esteem, understanding that this pattern is widespread, and that there is no placing of blame here.

Here, we have the opportunity to be loving and kind to ourselves, to accept our felt emotions, and to let them flow through rather than get stuck as "issues in the tissues."

The first step in acceptance is knowing there is absolutely nothing wrong with you. Perfection is not part of the human journey, and this journey doesn't come with instructions! Remember that your subconscious mind (the habit mind) is responsible for at least 95% of your daily choices and behaviors, and receives the vast majority of its deep programming by the time we reach seven years old (Lipton, 2015).

This is because our brainwave frequency changes after this age. Instead of learning by soaking everything up like a sponge with our theta brain waves, we move more decisively into beta brainwaves, and start learning by repetition. Everybody experiences emotional turmoil at some stage, and our subconscious habits can keep us stuck repeating the same patterns. Knowing you are not alone, and are simply and perfectly human, will help you to be kinder to yourself.

Notice when you see behaviors that trigger you reflected in others, remembering we are all mirrors of each other, and we are all teachers and students in our own way, here to learn from one another.

Take a moment so that you can respond and not (over)react. If stressed out, you're likely over-sensitive, and your emotions are heightened; in this state, you can easily misinterpret a situation. If you are confronted or challenged by an event, take a beat, and use your breath. Give yourself some breathing space before you speak.

If you need clarity, ask politely and in a neutral tone before formulating your response.

You can break these patterns by identifying your habitual reactions to things that trigger your stress and anxiety. Remember, it is often not *what* you say but *how* you say it that sends the loudest message. Your tone can belie your words.

What Are Your Triggers, Where Did They Come From?

For many of us, it helps to bring conscious understanding to subconscious patterns. Explore your own reactions and feelings with sincerity; put together a toolkit from the practices and techniques in this book to shine a light on the patterns causing you anxiety.

As an adult, you enter a theta brainwave state in meditation and sleep, so this is a great time to reprogram some of those patterns. The brain becomes sponge-like again, soaking up new ideas and information. Audio recordings to support healthier patterns like rejuvenating sleep, self-belief, and reaching your goals are said to be more efficient if listened to when deeply relaxed or sleeping.

Make sure that you don't let guilt or shame linger if you revert to negative behaviors now and then when you're on a journey of self-healing. Allow these feelings to be seen and acknowledged but let them swiftly pass through you as you accept your humanity. Accept that life is sometimes stormy, and use your self-healing toolkit to ride the waves. Transformation is possible simply by putting one foot in front of the other, using the techniques shared here, and knowing that these self-healing techniques have the potential to open you up to a whole new level of inner freedom and self-love.

Meditation

- Set aside time to meditate as often as you can. Start with just a few minutes a day.
- Find a quiet spot where you won't be disturbed by noise or interruptions. If noises do happen, that's okay; just let them be.
- Sit cross-legged if you can; this position grounds you firmly. At the same time, you should not be too comfortable; you don't want to become drowsy. If you can't sit cross-legged, just make sure you feel grounded. Don't relax too much back into soft cushions, though. You want to stay alert.
- Breathe deeply and close your eyes or gaze down.
- Now, concentrate on your body: Start at the feet, then move your focus up your legs and notice any tension or discomfort. Move your focus to your spine. Keep it comfortably aligned, but remember, your spine has a natural curve.
- Move your attention to your chest. Open your chest by moving your shoulders back. Lift the chin slightly, but don't look up.
- Be aware of your arms and hands; let your hands rest on your legs, palms facing up as if to receive a blessing.
- Your mind might wander; that is okay. Bring it back and concentrate on your breath and the sensation of your breath in your nostrils.
- Scan your body for other sensations, like the sun's heat or the wind's soft touch. Listen to the sounds around you. If you hear noises, don't judge them. Let them be and return your attention to your body and senses.
- If you feel pain, breathe into it. If the pain is too sharp, adapt your posture slightly.
- Be aware of your body and senses, and how they relate to your immediate environment.
- Your mind will wander, but it is no problem. Bring it back to your breath and body.

- Practice meditation as often as possible, starting with just five minutes in the morning. Notice the difference it makes to your day and your mood.
- As you grow into meditation, you can extend the practice.

Quick Reminder

- Finding your Zen gives you perspective and lets you remain calm when handling life's highs and lows.
- Journaling is an excellent way to relieve anxiety, because by writing down your negative thoughts and emotions, you can see them objectively and with less judgment. And your imagination and creativity can interplay to help you find solutions and expression.
- Your emotions (e-motions) are normal; you need to feel to heal. Use the techniques shared in this book to combat any fear of your emotions and let the energy in motion move through you.
- Acceptance is not resigning yourself to live with negativity; it helps you to be less critical of yourself and acknowledges the emotions that want to flow through you.

10

Yoga, A Wellness Journey

 Yoga is when every cell in the body sings the song of the soul.

B. K. S. Iyengar

Change Your Life With Yoga

YOGA IS A WORLD IN ITSELF, and exploring yoga can be the best decision of your life. There is no age limit, no required fitness level, and no dress code. With a yoga mat and a block (should you need it in some poses), your perspective on your body, and eventually on your life, could change right there on your mat.

Yoga is not a competitive sport— you want to win the silent race against premature aging. Yoga is not an Olympic sport, yet it opens worlds to people even in their seventies. If you are worried about injuries, a bad back, a wobbly knee, or a stiff neck, a yoga instructor will teach poses to protect you from injury and improve your core strength.

We usually associate the core with abdominal muscles, but the hip and lower back muscles form part of the core. Our core muscles start to lose flexibility already in our thirties. Fortunately, yoga can strengthen the core muscles, and you can start yoga at any age.

Core strength is essential for all sports activities and for simple everyday tasks, like picking up toys or pulling out a chair.

But yoga is much more than a gentle strengthening exercise. Yoga builds confidence and grace, with the breath leading every movement. The yoga system is around five thousand years old and was originally designed to harmonize your energy body through breath and focus. Through the practice of even simple yoga, you will better appreciate the gift of your body and its beautiful complexity.

A qualified yoga instructor is trained to help you. Choose a soft-spoken, experienced, yoga teacher who will guide you into your practice with kindness. You might later enjoy more dynamic teachers and the challenges of more intense forms of yoga like hot yoga, but while you are still vulnerable, choose:

- kindness from a teacher with a gentle touch;
- kindness to your body on its journey to rediscover its strength and suppleness;
- kindness to yourself as you get to know your inner world through your practice.

A Simple Beginner's Yoga Practice

Alternatively, consider online classes or begin with the seven poses below. As your yoga journey continues, you will discover that yoga's purpose is not getting a pose right, but is rather the journey into the pose. Every time you practice a pose, you will find some new dimension in your breath, movement, or posture. And that's why you don't get tired of yoga: getting the pose right is irrelevant. How you move into the pose brings body awareness, gratitude, and peace.

Mountain Pose (Tadasana)

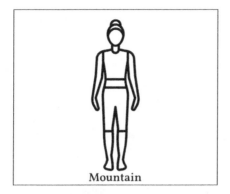

Stand with your two feet together, all four corners of your feet firmly grounded. With legs straight and while engaging the thigh muscles, tuck your tailbone. Your arms hang straight at your sides, palms facing forward.

Mountain pose is the foundation for many other yoga poses, and is all about alignment, balance, and trust. It seems deceptively easy, but close your eyes during mountain pose, and you might suddenly lose your balance. This pose combines aligning your body, maintaining balance, and trusting your feet to support you.

Child's Pose (Balasana)

Begin by kneeling (with padding if needed). Inhale, and lower your upper body slowly onto your thighs, or as far as you can manage, keeping your bottom on your heels. Keep your arms extended in front of you, placing your forehead on the mat if possible, in a position of surrender. Inhale and exhale deeply while allowing yourself a moment of rest.

Child's pose stretches the spine, legs, and hips. It stimulates blood flow through the body, from the head to the toes. It's good for digestion and takes you back to the playfulness of childhood.

Cat/Cow Pose (Marjarysana to Bitilasana)

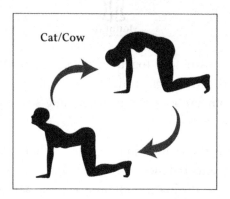

Start on all fours, hands under the shoulders, knees under the hips (tabletop position). Keep your spine straight and engage your tummy muscles. Exhale and round the spine, looking down like a cat. In your mind, try to attach the abdominal muscles to the spine. Tuck your chin slightly, but be careful not to tense the neck muscles. Inhale deeply, drop the tummy down, arch the spine downward and lift the tailbone. Also, lift the head.

Don't rush through these movements; take it slow to prevent muscle strain.

Cat/cow is a fun movement mimicking two beloved animals: a cat's balancing ability to always land on its feet, and a cow's groundedness. Moving between the poses with your breath improves balance and strengthens the spine, neck, hips, and abdomen while massaging the belly organs. Finding physical balance opens the way to emotional balance and calms the mind.

Downward-Facing Dog (Adho Mukha Svanasana)

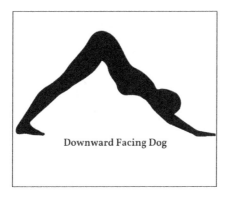

Downward Facing Dog

Down dog might be the most recognizable of all yoga poses, and not without reason. It takes courage to try this pose and show your bum to the world, and this is what yoga is all about: concentrating on your breath, your body, and the stillness within, regardless of what the world thinks.

Start by kneeling with your knees under your hips. Place your hands in front of you, slightly wider than shoulder width, fingers spread so that they all take weight evenly. Tuck your toes under and lift your hips to form a triangle with your tailbone at the highest point. Your chest should ideally move toward the legs. The feet are about hip-width apart.

In the beginning, your heels would probably lift. Let it be; your heels might come down over the next weeks or months. If not, remember it's not about getting your heels to touch the ground; it's about stretching your back, shoulders, arms, hamstrings, calves, and the tendons in your hands and feet.

Down dog does so much more than give you a good stretch. Because the heart is higher than the head, your blood circulates through the entire body, energizing and calming you. This pose has many health benefits: it clears the sinuses, builds bone density, and helps digestion. For those of us sitting at a computer most of the day, downward dog helps the body to correct a rounded back and tense shoulders.

However, most importantly, it promotes balance in the body and the mind. You can't help but get a somewhat lighter perspective on life's pressures with your head down and bottom up.

Warrior I (Virabhadrasana I)

Begin warrior 1 in mountain pose. Inhale and step your left foot back to come into a lunge. Bend the right leg with the knee over the ankle. Inhale and engage your abdominal muscles while you lift your arms up and overhead. Exhale and turn your left toes outward at a 45-degree angle. Inhale and pull your shoulders back and downward. Don't turn your hips to the left; keep them facing to the front. If you feel unstable, engage your abdominal muscles and press firmly into the outside of your back foot. Repeat the same for the other side of the body.

This power pose strengthens the legs, arms, and abdominal muscles. Because so many different body parts have to work together, it teaches concentration, balance, and body awareness. It gives you an acute perception of where every part of your body is and connects your mind to your body. Warrior pose is not about aggression; it is about empowerment and assertiveness to face the world with courage.

Warrior II (Virabhadrasana II)

Warrior II

Warrior II builds on warrior I. Bend your front leg, knee over ankle. Step the other leg back, turning the back foot out at a 90-degree angle. Turn your torso sideways and stretch the arms in opposite directions, parallel to the floor and in line with your shoulders. Face forward and focus on your outstretched fingers. The sideways movement opens the hips and adds flexibility.

This pose strengthens the entire body. Warrior 11 requires physical stillness for the duration of the pose. Being able to hold and not relax the tension paves the way for mental stillness amid life's challenges.

Corpse Pose (Savasana)

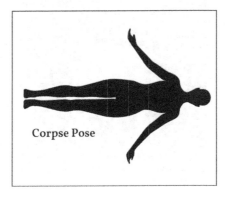

Corpse Pose

This pose is every yogi's dream, and it is traditionally the final pose in a class—and the most important. You lie on your back, totally relaxed. Your feet fall sideways; your arms are relaxed next to the body, with the palms facing up. Sink your back and torso into your mat and relax your facial muscles and scalp.

Although relaxing, corpse pose is more than merely resting after a strenuous yoga session. Corpse pose offers rest for the body and stillness for the mind. If you struggle with this, concentrate on relaxing your muscles one by one. Start at the toes and mindfully wiggle and relax them. Move your attention from the toes to the feet and the ankles until your whole body is relaxed.

This pose is ideal for when you struggle to sleep. Try this next time you find it difficult to switch your mind off at bedtime. However, take your time with the gradual relaxing of your body. The tension in your body and mind has built up over the entire day or even over several days. Allow your body time to unwind and become calm gradually.

This gift is an audio recording to guide you to explore your own deep and rejuvenating Savasana.

Use the code SelfHealingGift for free access:

Unblock Your Chakras

Chapter 1 describes the energy body, made up of energy centers known as chakras. They are part of each of us, representing our unique bioenergy field, which in turn connects us to the collective energy field of everything and everyone around us. This field is packed with information that is being exchanged all the time. Think about when you can feel your friend or your partner's stress without speaking to them. Or when you can instinctively feel they are bubbling with excitement over something without them saying a word.

Suppressed emotion, things we've stuffed down and didn't deal with at the time, is a major cause of blockage in the free flow and exchange in the energy body. If the flow of energy is blocked, you can imagine the organs and body systems supplied will receive less than they need. So over time, if these issues are not dealt with, the physical body will be affected by this reduced flow.

Each chakra corresponds to specific emotions and to the surrounding organs. Yoga is an excellent way to unblock chakras, as this is what the yoga system was originally designed for.

Here is a suggested Seven Chakra Yoga Sequence to support a balanced flow of energy through your energy body and helpful adjuncts to your practice.

Unblocking Muladhara (Base) Chakra

Forward Fold Butterfly

The following emotions might indicate that the base chakra is blocked: anxiety, insecurity, feeling fearful, and feeling unsafe. You may have issues with your bowels, bladder, colon, lower back, and legs.

- Try these yoga poses: Forward fold and Bhadrasana (butterfly pose). As you are in the pose, imagine the energy of the base chakra providing you with stability and connecting you to the earth.
- Colors and healing stones: red and black; ruby, obsidian, and red jasper.
- Foods: red fruit and vegetables (tomatoes, chilies, strawberries, and red peppers) and root vegetables like carrots, beets, radishes, garlic, onions, and parsnips.

Unblocking the Svadhisthana (Second Chakra, Relationships)

Lack of or changes in your sexual energy usually indicate that the second chakra is unbalanced. If you can't find joy in creativity, feel shy and inhibited in social situations, or are not having luck on the dating scene, work at balancing the second chakra.

Half Moon   Goddess

- Try these yoga poses: Half moon or goddess pose, and feel and imagine the energy center at the level of the pelvis being charged up.

- Colors and healing stones: orange and red; place a garnet, carnelian, bloodstone, or orange-colored calcite on your stomach below the belly button.
- Foods: all orange foods like pumpkin, carrots, and sweet potato; fruits like oranges, papaya, and mango.

Unblocking Manipura (Solar Plexus) Chakra

The solar plexus chakra is in the stomach area. An unhealthy appetite is a near-certain indication that this chakra needs unblocking. Imbalance manifests as digestive problems, bloating, gas, or acid reflux.

You may feel low in self-esteem, find yourself easily bullied, or lack drive and willpower.

Triangle   Boat

- Try these yoga poses: triangle and boat pose and feel that golden sun energy of the solar plexus strengthening you from within.
- Colors and healing stones: yellow and gold; tiger's eye, citrine and yellow calcite.
- Foods: yellow bell peppers, bananas, and pineapples; spices like ginger and turmeric.

Unblocking the Anahata (Heart) Chakra

Problems with loss, love, and forgiveness can unbalance the heart chakra. It can physically manifest as physical pain, tightness in the chest area, or breathing issues.

Try these yoga poses: anahata (heart melting) pose or sphinx.

- Colors and healing stones: green; wear emeralds, jade, and green calcite, or peridot over the heart.
- Foods: green leafy vegetables like spinach, kale, cucumber, peas, artichoke, and zucchini.

Unblocking Vishuddha (Throat) Chakra

The throat chakra is the connection between your body and mind; thus, the link between your emotional and physical needs. It affects thyroid function and causes pain in the throat, jaw, cheeks, and mouth area. If this chakra is blocked, you will find it difficult to speak and communicate freely, contributing to your anxiety.

Shoulder Stand   Locked Bridge

- Try these yoga poses: shoulder stands, locked bridge. Feel the energy around the throat, allow your breaths to be a little more shallow in these positions.
- Color and healing stones: sky blue, lapis lazuli, aquamarine, turquoise, and celestite.
- Foods: all berries in blue and purple shades; soothing teas, kelp, wheatgrass, and ginseng.

Unblocking the Ajna (Third Eye) Chakra

An unbalanced third eye chakra manifests as vision problems, memory issues, struggle to focus, headaches, and loss of intuition. A blocked third eye chakra may also cause narrow-mindedness and a lack of a balanced worldview. Check in with yourself when you are increasingly impatient with others. Overthinking, racing, and looping thoughts can get you stuck on specific issues.

Eagle   Lotus

- Try lotus position, eagle, and silent meditation. (Refer to the previous chapter for guidance on a simple yoga practice.) Feel the energetic focus at the level of the third eye.
- Refer to the previous chapter for guidance on a simple meditation practice.
- Color and healing stones: a purple-blue to dark purple; sapphire, amethyst, lapis lazuli, and sugilite.
- Foods: purple foods like plums, eggplants, and grapes.

Unblocking the Sahasrara (Crown) Chakra

When the crown chakra is blocked, you feel spiritually flat and disconnected from your source; you can feel depressed and isolated. Reflect on what is most important right now. Is there a scarcity mentality going on? A primary focus on material wealth or status? Usually, it is a sign that the crown chakra is blocked, because you are not giving enough attention to higher goals and aspirations for spiritual growth and expanding consciousness.

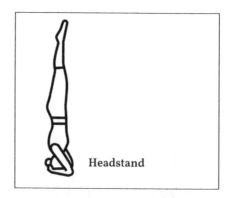

Headstand

- Try a headstand if this is within your practice. Focus on the energy center at the crown of your head.
- You can also do any meditation posture with your focus on the crown of your head, feel and imagine the thousand-petalled lotus unfurling into bloom.

- Colors and healing stones: purple and white; diamonds, moonstones, amethysts, and clear crystals.
- Foods: fasting helps clear the crown chakra; listen to your body and fast responsibly.

Quick Reminder

- Breath is central to your yoga practice.
- Yoga benefits the entire body and strengthens the core, which is vital for even the smallest movement.
- Try the seven beginner poses in yoga.
- Yoga is about letting your breath lead your body and enjoying the journey. Do not strive for perfection; instead, concentrate on the beauty of body, breath, and mind working together.
- Bottled-up emotional and mental stress blocks energy flow and can eventually lead to physical imbalances.
- Meditation helps to unblock the crown chakra, which is responsible for spiritual well-being and a feeling of connection to all that is.

11

Savor Your Sunshine

 Your vision becomes clear when you look inside your heart. Who looks outside, dreams. Who looks inside, awakens.

Carl Gustav Jung

Nurture Your Happiness

ULTIMATELY, we all want to be happy, and the secret to happiness lies in concentrating on the good in your life. Focus on the small things that bring a smile to your lips, and you will find unsuspected joy everywhere.

It might surprise you that happiness does not lie in achieving your dreams or having money or status. True happiness originates from your inner world.

Honestly Observe How You Judge and Compare

Are you proud of your high standards in life?

Are you quick to judge other people and their actions?

How is your inner critic? Are you the hardest on yourself?

A tendency to judge might say more about you than those you may criticize.

Think of those around you as your mirrors. Criticism of others may reflect your own negative patterns. Psychologists refer to this phenomenon as negativity bias. We often naturally see the negative in ourselves and others. However, we can consciously change our mindset to look for the good in ourselves and others and to look for what we admire and respect instead.

Ways to Overcome Negativity

Self-love and acceptance are discussed all the way through this book, which is an indication of how important it is to your well-being. Ask yourself: Can you extend this acceptance to others despite their shortcomings? Allowing for others' mistakes and noticing when you sit in judgment, this noticing is the first step. What is the mirror that is held up to you when facing a difficult interaction? It can be a challenging lens to look through at first; however, when you practice this technique, you will start to know yourself much better, and that deep understanding of others and how life teaches you will become clearer.

Take a moment to respond and not (over)react. If stressed out, you're likely over-sensitive, and your emotions are heightened. In this state, you could easily misinterpret a situation. If you are confronted or challenged by an event, take a beat, and use your breath. Give yourself some breathing space before you speak. If you need clarity, ask politely and in a neutral tone before formulating your response.

Remember, it is so often not what you say but how you say it that sends the loudest message. Your tone can belie your words.

When you catch yourself judging others, check your thought patterns and emotions. You will be surprised how your emotional world influences how you view others. Working on self-acceptance is essential in building positive and harmonious relationships. Cultivate kindness to yourself and you will develop a more accepting attitude toward others.

Beware of Social Comparison

We are conditioned from an early age to compare ourselves to our peers. Often, we judge ourselves as coming up short; meaning, we measure our achievements, education, and appearance to someone we think is better than us. It explains our obsession with celebrities, and, not surprisingly, affects our sense of self-worth.

The opposite is also detrimental: feeling superior and rating someone as not being on our level. How we see others reflects how we see ourselves, equally vulnerable to criticism and judgment.

Journaling can help with our perspective on ourselves and our social environment. Identify the things that contribute to any self-doubt. Are there qualities that you feel are not up to scratch? Are these things truly important to you? Or have you gotten lost in a quest to fit into a social circle that does not share your true, Soul-centered values? Let your notes guide you in finding your way back to your true nature.

Journaling can help you identify the obstacles to your emotional well-being. Use the techniques in this book to change what you can, but, above all, to guide yourself to self-acceptance. Remember, you can restructure the neural pathways in the brain by cultivating positive thought patterns. Reread Chapter 7 and remind yourself that you can change negative thought patterns.

Gratitude

Being grateful opens the heart, makes you happy, and brings more to be grateful for.

Gratitude holds a particular frequency. It opens the heart center, and by practicing gratitude daily, we bring in more people, events, and things we can appreciate and be grateful for. Gratitude supports you in building self-acceptance and healthy relationships. Once again, journaling, especially in those precious minutes before sleep, is a great way to rewire the subconscious mind into an attitude of gratitude. It is a written reminder of all the good in your life that will give you perspective when you hit difficult times.

Research shows that grateful people are happier and have fewer health problems. Interestingly, people who appreciate their health also take better care of themselves. They eat more carefully, exercise regularly, and have annual health checks. They acknowledge their blessings and don't concentrate on what they don't have. It makes an enormous difference to your emotional life to be grateful, even in the face of adversity.

Practice gratitude by consciously cultivating it, such as writing a thank you note to someone, offering a prayer of thanks, or meditating on gratitude.

- Do not allow your thanks to be meaningless words only. When you thank someone, make it specific, even if only in your own mind. Note what you are grateful for: passing the milk or reaching for an item high on a supermarket shelf.
- Meditation is an opportunity to remember your blessings mindfully. Use meditation to offer thanks for the blessings in your life. Gratitude is enormously powerful.

Gratitude Practice

Chapter 8 gives guidelines for meditation practice. Adapt this practice to cultivate gratitude.

- Sit comfortably in your preferred meditation pose.
- Concentrate on your breath and be alert to your senses. Try to name the pleasant sensations in your surroundings.
- You can now move your focus to something beautiful or pleasant you have seen or experienced during the day or week. Remember the sight or experience in as much

detail as possible and say an inward thank you for its beauty.

- Move on to the next sense, and try to relive the smell of something pleasant: your baby after a bath, the flowers on your way to the bus stop, or your first cup of coffee of the day.
- Listen to the sounds around you; enjoy the bird song. Think of your favorite music. Hum the melody and say thank you for the beauty of sound.
- Write down everyone who contributed to making your day enjoyable, even in the slightest way. Name the interaction and thank the person in your mind.
- End your meditation practice by breathing deeply and thank your body for its remarkable ability to support your life.

Gratitude brings grace, and grace magnetizes connection and joy.

Practicing gratitude will raise your spirits and lessen your anxiety. It is an excellent antidote to irritation and frustration, the primary cause of overt or passive aggression. Your sleep quality will improve, as will your empathy when dealing with other people. You will gradually notice that your attitude of gratitude evokes positivity from others, which in return will boost your confidence and self-esteem.

Dr. Robert A. Emmons, a world-renowned specialist in gratitude, reports that gratitude has two components. Firstly, it confirms that there is goodness in our lives. Secondly, it emphasizes that goodness sprouts from a source outside the self (Ackerman, 2017). It enhances our sense of gratitude to know that we are part of a greater humanity and that life would be dreary without the support of others.

Gratitude is an attitude rather than a fleeting sensation. At its best, it nestles deep into your heart and contributes to shaping you as a human being. Being grateful will support you in facing the challenges that come your way by deepening your resolve to overcome adversities, and it brings a frequency of fortitude amid crises.

Finding Joy

Joy is an exuberant emotion of well-being, something the anxious or stressed-out person may struggle to experience. I want you to find your joy and happiness again.

How long has it been since you have felt passionate about something? Do you love your work? Are you passionate about a hobby and can't wait until you can resume your activity? When you live your passion, your brain releases endorphins, enhancing the joy you experience.

Being True To Yourself

If you can't remember the last time you were really excited about something, it is time to take a step back and give yourself space to contemplate. Leave your problems at the door for half an hour and remember what makes you happy. Think back on happier times and list things that truly bring you joy. At the same time, consider what is standing in the way of your joy; it may help to write this down.

Chapter 8 tells you how journaling can help you to find clarity. Is there a way that you can find, using the techniques shared in this book, to accept the things you can't change and be at peace with them so that repetitive negative thought loops don't rule your life?

Look at these obstacles to your happiness realistically. Think of your strengths and possible changes you can implement to navigate your challenges, but do not rush through these steps; take your time and consider them carefully.

Once you have clarity on dealing with and accepting the trials that may present obstacles, concentrate on getting your passion back into your life.

Explore your inner world; you can do this through meditation and reflection. What did you love as a child? What lit you up as a teenager? This process can help you to delve deep to find your true passions.

We often neglect our deep passions when we constantly live in over-drive or spend a lot of time and effort meeting others' expectations and people-pleasing. Our true passions can fall by the wayside and end up forgotten.

Write down what you love; formulate a personal vision statement on what and how you will find the time and means for activities you are passionate about. Be realistic in exploring your passion. Can you make a career of your passion? Do you have the training? Would you like to undertake new studies? Do your family setup and responsibilities allow you to follow your dream? Don't be discouraged; look deeper and find how you can live your passion, even in a small way to start with.

You might not be able to sell your home and travel the world, but you can start reading about different cultures and traditions. If your passion is acting, you could join a local theater group. Even take up casual swimming if you can't be an Olympic swimmer.

If you can't pursue your passion full-time, try a hobby in the same field. Practicing a hobby might not be your real dream, but it is a creative outlet and will bring you joy and nourish your Soul. If you are not ready for drastic changes, start with smaller steps. Use your time management skills to make time for your hobby.

You have to be true to your deepest values and norms.

Quick Reminder

- If you are spinning in anxiety, even when it is simmering in the background, you stop noticing the small joys in life, and the spiral can take you downward.
- We can reconstruct negative thought patterns to make way for greater enjoyment.
- Self-acceptance is a prerequisite for being less self-critical; being kind to yourself is the first step to empathy directed outward.
- Comparing yourself to others is a habit you can recognize and shift, as it can destroy your confidence and self-worth.

- Practicing gratitude makes you happier and healthier.
- Journaling and meditation are excellent ways to remember your blessings.
- Delve deep to find your passions; they reflect your core values and who you are.

Afterword

I am not what happened to me, I am what I choose to
become.

Carl Gustav Jung

AT THE END of this unique journey to eliminate anxiety and enjoy
life to the fullest, let us remind ourselves of the steps along the way.

At the start of this book, I shared alarming mental health statistics.
The many techniques shared in this book can change things for you
and deepen your self-healing capacity and ability to discover your
inner strength.

An essential realization is that emotions, including anxiety, are
normal. They are powerful energies moving through your system,
needing acknowledgment. Another vital part of the story of the
human condition is that everyone at some point in their life will
experience sadness, anxiety, grief, anger, abandonment, heartbreak,
you name it! And on the flip side of this, we have all felt the heights
of happiness, joy, and love. Most of us are not taught how to
process our amazing emotions; they can feel overwhelming, fright-

ening, and too big for us sometimes. This book has provided proven, safe resources for you to equip yourself to work with your powerful emotional self without denying it and without pushing your feelings aside. The work contained in these pages is here for you to dip into, refer back to, and practice from as much as you need to build your resources.

Early on, I introduced the concept of the energy body, the unseen subtle energy field that enfolds, infuses, and connects us, and the seven chakras that form its skeleton. Each chakra has its own qualities and responsibilities; the existence of this energy field is becoming undeniable. It is within our power to work with the subtle energies of the body to support truly holistic health and the free flow of life force energy.

Although feelings of anxiety may be longstanding, often, the best starting point is practical. Organize your day with your priorities at heart to take the tiresome burden of constant decision-making off your shoulders.

When you sort out the chaos of your overcrowded day, work demands, and the needs of your household, your stress levels will immediately come down, leaving you the time and the energy for more focus on what is present for you right now.

So often, we rush mindlessly from one task to another, fueling our spiraling thoughts and growing anxiety with even more stress. Take a step back, consider what is important to you, delve deeper, and identify your priorities. Knowing yourself, loving yourself, and setting priorities accordingly are the starting point of effective time management and reclaiming your inner calm.

We moved on to discovering the connection between sleep deprivation and anxiety. Sleep is a non-negotiable when it comes to self-healing. Brain activity does not stop when you sleep. When you don't sleep well, the subconscious mind cannot process the day's memories, emotions, and events. Instead of waking up refreshed, you begin a new day, stressed and tired.

Based on my work with clients over the years and on a body of scientific evidence, I highlight the hazard of using electronic devices in the hours up to bedtime. Screens and charging lights emit a frequency of blue light that interferes with sleep, so it's advisable to keep all devices out of the bedroom overnight. A bedtime routine is vital to prepare the body and mind for rest. Follow this book's tips on good sleep, and you will see results within a few weeks. As a bonus, your cognitive function will improve, and you might even find it easier to stabilize your weight.

In a world where social media has become the reference point for how we want to look and live, we can fall into the trap of comparison, and our mood can drop if we are critical of ourselves. Of course, social media has many benefits, but be careful of false and often fabricated trends. Even friends and neighbors can have heavily filtered social media accounts, which can pull us under into a feeling of lack. Instead, consider the body positivity trend to help you find your inner happiness with your outer beauty and ideal body weight, recognizing that celebrity and influence have little to do with happiness.

Your diet and your emotional ups and downs are connected. Fluctuations in your blood sugar significantly contribute to your emotional state over the day. As an additional benefit, managing your sugars over the day can help you with weight control by keeping you feeling fuller for longer. Refined and processed foods release sugar quickly, causing glucose spikes followed by sharp drops, which come with sugar cravings, fatigue, and irritability. Lean protein, healthy fat, and wholegrain, high-fiber foods release sugar gradually, so you're less prone to sugar highs and crashes which can leave you "*hangry*". Stabilizing your blood sugar levels and keeping your hunger at bay will help prevent the emotional ups and downs of the blood sugar rollercoaster.

As you start to make different choices for your body and mind, your self-care will open your eyes to the complexity and wonder of your whole system. You will discover how movement is linked to your emotional health because your body releases feel-good endorphins during activity. The interplay between your emotional and physical health will also become more clear. By bringing firstly awareness and then balance to your diet and your blood sugar levels over the day, you will be able to combat anxiety from a new angle.

We breathe all the time and rarely pay attention to it. Bringing awareness to your breath can instantly lower stress levels by bringing more of the "rest, digest, heal" side of the autonomic nervous system into play through deep, diaphragmatic breathing. Breath connects every cell in the body—muscles, limbs, organs, the nervous system, and the brain. Therefore, our physical and mental processes influence each other in a beautiful symphony if we consciously connect simply through the breath.

Psychology can be intimidating, but Chapter 7 uses easily understandable language to guide you into making sense of recurring worrying thoughts. An additional practical emergency toolkit is described with techniques to use in public if panic threatens to overwhelm you.

The allure surrounding Eastern healing methods, like mindfulness and yoga, are demystified in Part Two. Yoga was designed in ancient times, and its original purpose was to harmonize the energetic, mental, emotional, and physical levels. Yoga clears blockages and opens the chakras. The breath leads in yoga and quiets emotional turmoil while enhancing physical flexibility and grace. The power of breath, the value of building core strength, and the complex connection between the mind, brain, and body allow clear and strong energy to flow through each chakra.

Ultimately, this book aims to be accessible to insightful women who may be trapped in anxiety but who are smart enough to recognize the benefit of working with your incredible body's self-healing ability. You've been given the tools and techniques to find your *joie de vivre.* In essence, to regain control of your emotions, find harmony in your relationships and responsibilities, and explore your magnificent inner world.

As you begin to heal using these techniques, you will see that the changes you experience not only impact you. As you feel your energetic frequency rise, as your connection with your inner wisdom grows, it will ripple out to those around you, magnetizing new connections and solutions toward you. As you experience deep gratitude, you will uncover joy and peace like never before.

My hope is that by using these tools, you will start to notice that you are empowered to truly feel and to be every aspect of you without shame, guilt, or worry.

I warmly invite you to join an online community of like-hearted women, all awakening self-love and trust. Join in to ask questions and discover more self-healing techniques for your inner transformation:

We have been together on a journey, but it doesn't stop here...

Help someone else take control of their thoughts and emotions and know they are not alone.

As you start applying the strategies shared in this book, you may feel more like sharing your new sense of confidence and empowerment with others readers.

Simply by leaving a review of this book on Amazon, you will help other women see life through a more positive lens, so they can embrace thoughts and emotions that lead to more peace amid the rat race.

Thank you for your help.

Together, we can help others master their powerful e-motions, to be more connected to the body and act instead of react, and embrace the Self-Healing techniques that will help them achieve their dreams.

>>> Click Here To Leave Your Review On Amazon <<<

Scan The QR Code To Leave Your Review On Amazon Today

About The Author

Meet Dr. Samantha Wellappili

MBCHB MRCGP DRCOG DFSRH DipION
**Medical Doctor, Lifestyle Medicine
Specialist, Soul Purpose Coach,
Nutritionist, Yoga Therapist, Writer,
Energy Medicine Practitioner, Medi-
tation Facilitator**

Dr. Samantha Wellappili, the author of
Master Resilience to Burnout and Health
Hacks, among other works, lives by the sea in Brighton, England,
and is a happily practicing Lifestyle Medicine Doctor with a love of
adventure within and without.

She brings warmth and breadth of experience in family medicine to
her books, plus her transformational 1:1 mentorship and coaching,
where she supports women who seem to "have it all" yet struggle
with anxiety and feelings of not being good enough to overcome
these obstacles. Dr. Sam uses tailored techniques for each client to
realize their alignment with their higher self and integrate this influ-

ence into daily life, so creating and manifesting is effortless, and fuelled by the flow of life itself without the specter of fear, anxiety, and self-doubt keeping them stuck.

She has over 15 years of experience in the co-creation of deeply rooted self-worth, leading the way to discover Soul Purpose and how to align with this for greater joy and fulfillment.

You can visit her online at www.lifeandsoulmedicine.com or on Instagram (@drsamanthawellappili)

Free Book Offer:

If you've enjoyed this book, I'd like you to enjoy my previous book with my compliments.

Master Resilience to Burnout and Feel Like Yourself Again is a concise "Mini Book of Burnout" sharing the seven secrets to burnout recovery for modern day superwomen:

References

5 Time management personality types and actions to improve. (n.d.). Deepstash https://deepstash.com/article/1202/5-time-management-personality-types-and-actions-to-improve

8 Frankincense essential oil uses and benefits for healing. (2021 October 30). Dr. Axe. https://draxe.com/essential-oils/what-is-frankincense/

9 Benefits of yoga. (n.d.). Johns Hopkins Medicine. https://www.hopkinsmedicine.org/health/wellness-and-prevention/9-benefits-of-yoga

9 Ways to calm your anxiety and anxious thoughts. (2022 March 24). Cleveland Clinic. https://health.clevelandclinic.org/is-anxiety-ruling-your-life-try-9-ways-to-keep-it-at-bay/

7 Grounding techniques. (2020 April). Vanier College. https://www.vaniercollege.qc.ca/student-services/files/2020/04/7-Grounding-Techniques.pdf

10 Reasons why time management is important. (n.d.). Brainbridge. https://www.brainbridge.be/en/news/10-reasons-why-time-management-is-important

25 Grounding techniques for anxiety. (n.d.). Choose Mental Health. https://choosementalhealth.org/25-grounding-techniques-for-anxiety/

Abrahamsen, S. (2017 November 30). *How to untangle your mind with a brain dump.* Little Coffee Fox. https://littlecoffeefox.com/brain-dump/

Aerobic exercise: Top 10 reasons to get physical. (n.d.). https://www.mayoclinic.org/healthy-lifestyle/fitness/in-depth/aerobic-exercise/art-20045541

Ackerman, C.E. (2017 February 28). *What is gratitude and why is it so important?* Positive Psychology. https://positivepsychology.com/gratitude-appreciation/

Aggarwal, J. (n.d.). DSM-5: *Everything you need to know about the latest diagnostic criteria.* MantraCare. https://mantracare.org/therapy/anxiety/dsm-5-anxiety/#Defining_Anxiety

Alcohol and anxiety. (n.d.). Drink Aware UK. https://www.drinkaware.co.uk/facts/health-effects-of-alcohol/mental-health/alcohol-and-anxiety

Anderson, S. (n.d.). *A beginner's guide to chakras.* Yoga International. https://yogainternational.com/article/view/a-beginners-guide-to-chakras

Are you drinking enough water? (n.d.). Medical West. https://www.medicalwesthospital.org/are-you-drinking-enough-water.php

Ash, M. (2011 April). *Is this a perfect functional meal for mucosal tolerance?* Clinical Education. https://www.clinicaleducation.org/documents/apple_tolergenic_food.pdf

References

Automatic Negative Thoughts (ANTs) and unhelpful thinking styles (n.d.). MindWell. https://www.mindwell-leeds.org.uk/myself/exploring-your-mental-health/anxiety/challenge-negative-thoughts/automatic-negative-thoughts-ants-and-unhelpful-thinking-styles/

Balan, J. (n.d.). *11 Impacts of blood glucose levels on mood.* Ultrahuman. https://blog.ultrahuman.com/blog/the-impact-of-blood-glucose-levels-on-mood

Bauer, B.A., (n.d.). *Valerian: A safe and effective herbal sleep aid?* Mayo Clinic. https://www.mayoclinic.org/diseases-conditions/insomnia/expert-answers/valerian/faq-20057875

Being aware of automatic negative thoughts. (n.d.). MindWell. https://www.mindwell-leeds.org.uk/myself/exploring-your-mental-health/depression/challenging-negative-thinking/

Brazier, Y. (2017 March 20). *Aromatherapy: What you need to know.* MedicalNewsToday. https://www.medicalnewstoday.com/articles/10884

Burns, Karima. (2017 December 31). *Breath of life.* About Islam. https://aboutislam.net/muslim-issues/science-muslim-issues/breath-of-life/

Burton, N. (n.d.). *How to unblock chakras: A complete guide to getting clear from root to crown.* Goalcast. https://www.goalcast.com/how-to-unblock-chakras/

Cassata, C. (n.d.). *8 ways to accept yourself.* PsychCentral. https://psychcentral.com/lib/ways-to-accept-yourself

Cassidy, S. (2021 August 24). *7 Ways to accept and appreciate your body.* Today. https://www.today.com/health/7-ways-learn-accept-appreciate-your-body-today-t228957

Cherry, K. (n.d.). *What is body positivity?* Verywellmind. https://www.verywellmind.com/what-is-body-positivity-4773402

Cherry, K. (n.d.). *What is intrinsic motivation?* Verywellmind. https://www.verywellmind.com/what-is-intrinsic-motivation-2795385

Costello, N. (2013 November 15). *The subtle struggle of savasana.* Yoga Journal.https://www.yogajournal.com/poses/corpse-pose/

Cronkleton, E. (2020 July 28). *Practicing lion's breath.* Healthline. https://www.healthline.com/health/practicing-lions-breath

Courtney. R. (n.d.). *Resonance frequency breathing.* Rosalba Courtney. https://www.rosalbacourtney.com/resonance-frequency-breathing/

Cuncic, A. (2021 October 26). *Negative thoughts: How to stop them.* VeryWellMind. https://www.verywellmind.com/how-to-change-negative-thinking-3024843

Davis, T., Sperber, S. (2021 August 2 2). *How to practice acceptance.* Psychology Today. https://www.psychologytoday.com/us/blog/click-here-happiness/202108/how-practice-acceptance

Deep Breathing to relieve acute stress. (n.d.). UPMC Life Changing Medicine. https://www.upmc.com/services/healthy-lifestyles/acute-stress/deep-breathing

Delgado, J. (2022 November 5). *Jackson's progressive muscular relaxation technique.* Psychology Spot. https://psychology-spot.com/jacobson-muscular-relaxation-techinque/

Durward, E. (2019 November 11). *5 Menopause symptoms made worse by stress.* A. Vogel. https://www.avogel.co.uk/health/menopause/videos/5-menopause-symptoms-made-worse-by-stress/

References

Easy time-management tips. (n.d.). NHS Inform. https://www.nhsinform.scot/healthy-living/mental-wellbeing/stress/easy-time-management-tip sections

Ede, H. (2020 May 30). *The link between your body's physical and mental health explained.* Physicians Alliance of Connecticut, Hartford Healthcare. https://physiciansallianceofconnecticut.com/blog/link-between-physical-and-mental-health/

Endorphins. (n.d.). Cleveland Clinic. https://my.clevelandclinic.org/health/body/23040-endorphins

Exercise and stress: Get moving to manage stress. (n.d.). Mayo Clinic. https://www.mayoclinic.org/healthy-lifestyle/stress-management/in-depth/exercise-and-stress/art-20044469

Exercising for stress and anxiety. (n.d.). ADAA. https://adaa.org/living-with-anxiety/managing-anxiety/exercise-stress-and-anxiety

Fabrega, M. (n.d.). *10 Ways to tame your monkey mind and stop mind chatter.* Daring to Live Fully. https://daringtolivefully.com/tame-your-monkey-mind

Fletcher, J. (2019 February 12). *How to use 4-7-8 breathing for anxiety.* MedicalNewsToday. https://www.medicalnewstoday.com/articles/324417

Fitness: Tips for staying motivated. (n.d.). Mayo Clinic. https://www.mayoclinic.org/healthy-lifestyle/fitness/in-depth/fitness/art-20047624

Fowler, P. (2022 January 17). *Breathing techniques for stress relief.* WebMD. https://www.webmd.com/balance/stress-management/stress-relief-breathing-techniques

Functional medicine matrix: organizing clinical imbalances. (n.d.). The Institute for Functional Medicine. https://www.ifm.org/news-insights/toolkit-functional-medicine-matrix/

Getting started with mindfulness. (n.d.). Mindful Healthy Mind, Healthy Life. https://www.mindful.org/meditation/mindfulness-getting-started/

Gizzi, C. (2018 June 12). 11 Extremely powerful Caroline Myss quotes to help you heal your heart. Fearless Soul. https://iamfearlesssoul.com/caroline-myss-quotes/

Giving thanks can make you happier. (2021 August 14). Harvard Health Publishing. https://www.health.harvard.edu/healthbeat/giving-thanks-can-make-you-happier

Goldman, R. (2020 July 21). *What is Jacobson's relaxation technique?* Healthline. https://www.healthline.com/health/what-is-jacobson-relaxation-technique

Greenfieldboyce, N. (2019 February 20). *The power of Martin Luther King Jr's anger.* Code Switch. https://www.npr.org/sections/codeswitch/2019/02/20/691298594/the-power-of-martin-luther-king-jr-s-anger

Gupta, S. (n.d.). *Calling all diabetics: Here's why you need to nosh fermented foods.* HealthShots. https://www.healthshots.com/healthy-eating/nutrition/heres-why-fermented-foods-are-the-best-foods-for-diabetics

Harper, C. (n.d.). *How to overcome comparison anxiety.* MyWellbeing. https://mywellbeing.com/therapy-101/how-to-overcome-comparison-anxiety

Hernandez, B. (n.d.). *Personal goal setting: Planning to live your life your way.* MindTools. https://www.mindtools.com/page6.html

Hernandez, B. (n.d.). *The 7 most effective ways of overcoming deadline stress.* Timehero. https://www.timehero.com/post/the-7-most-effective-ways-of-overcoming-deadline-stres

Holistic health goals vary by age. (2019 June 13). Nutraceuticals World. https://www.nu-

References

traceuticalsworld.com/contents/view_breaking-news/2019-06-13/holistic-health-goals-vary-by-age/

How do breathing exercises reduce stress? (2021 May 5). Calmer. https://www.thisiscalmer.com/blog/how-do-breathing-exercises-alleviate-stress

How to fall asleep faster and sleep better. (n.d.). NHS Better Health. https://www.nhs.uk/every-mind-matters/coronavirus/how-to-fall-asleep-faster-and-sleep-better/

Ismail, N. (n.d.). *Your guide to anxiety fidget toys.* Forbes Health. https://www.forbes.com/health/mind/fidget-toys-for-anxiety/

Is this an anxiety attack or heart attack? How to know. (2022 September 2). UPMC Health Beat. https://share.upmc.com/2018/02/anxiety-attack-or-heart-attack/

Jackson, C. (2019 May 23). *Can spirituality help depression? It serves as a protective barrier, improves symptoms, and offers a new outlook on life.* Thriveworks. https://thriveworks.com/blog/can-spirituality-help-depression/

Jacoby Zoldan, R. (2022 January 1). *7 Beginner yoga poses to get through your first class.* Daily Burn. https://dailyburn.com/life/fitness/beginner-yoga-poses-positions/

Journaling for mental health. (n.d.). University of Rochester Medical Center Health Encyclopedia. https://www.urmc.rochester.edu/encyclopedia/content.aspx?ContentID=4552&ContentTypeID=1

Knapp, A. (2012 May 4). *Why your brain isn't a computer.* Forbes. https://www.forbes.com/sites/alexknapp/2012/05/04/why-your-brain-isnt-a-computer/?sh=5c69348013e1

Kubala, J. (2020 August 10). *The 17 best food to lower (or regulate) your blood sugar.* Healthline. https://www.healthline.com/nutrition/foods-to-lower-blood-sugar

Laderer, A. (2020 July 10). *Shake it off—and other quick physical ways to squash anxiety.* Greatest. https://greatist.com/health/physical-anxiety-techniques

Leaf C. (n.d.). *Current clinical trials.* Mbghealth. https://drleaf.com/pages/current-clinical-trials

Leaf, C. (2021 March 8). *How are the mind & the brain different? A neuroscientist explains.* Mbghealth. https://www.mindbodygreen.com/articles/difference-between-mind-and-brain-neuroscientist

Leech, J. (n.d.). *10 Reasons to get more sleep.* Healthline. https://www.healthline.com/nutrition/10-reasons-why-good-sleep-is-important

Lindberg, S. (2018 August 31). *How to let go of things from the past.* Healthline. https://www.healthline.com/health/how-to-let-go

Lipton, B. (2015 April 24). *Is there a way to subconscious patterns?* Bruce Lipton.com. (https://www.brucelipton.com/there-way-change-subconscious-patterns/)

Lipton, B. (2005). *The biology of belief: Unleashing the power of consciousness, matter & miracles.* Hay House.

MacMillan, A. (2015 October 10). *The 7 body benefits of downward dog.* Daily Burn. https://dailyburn.com/life/fitness/downward-dog-health-benefits/

Marksberry, K. (2012 August 10). *Take a deep breath.* The American Institute of Stress. https://www.stress.org/take-a-deep-breath

Martin, S. (2016 January 26). *6 easy ways to stop criticizing and improve your relationships.* PsychCentral. https://psychcentral.com/blog/imperfect/2016/01/6-easy-ways-to-stop-criticizing-and-improve-your-relationships

References

Martin, S. (2008). *The power of the relaxation response.* American Psychological Association. https://www.apa.org/monitor/2008/10/relaxation

Mind/body connection: How your emotions affect your health. (n.d.). Familydoctor.org. https://familydoctor.org/mindbody-connection-how-your-emotions-affect-your-health/

Mind management. (n.d.). Brilliant Living. https://www.brilliantlivinghq.com/mind-management/

Morin, A. (2022 January 21). *A quick trick for becoming less judgmental.* Verywellmind. https://www.verywellmind.com/becoming-less-judgmental-friday-fix-the-verywell-mind-podcast-5216558

Morin, A. (2014 November 23). *7 Scientifically proven benefits of gratitude that will motivate you to give thanks year-round.* Forbes. https://www.forbes.com/sites/amymorin/2014/11/23/7-scientifically-proven-benefits-of-gratitude-that-will-motivate-you-to-give-thanks-year-round/?sh=30aed8df183c

Murphy, A. (2022 April 14). *How to find joy in life every single day.* Declutter The Mind. https://declutterthemind.com/blog/how-to-find-joy/

Nall, R. (2019 February 18). *Which essential oils can relieve anxiety?* MedicalNewsToday. https://www.medicalnewstoday.com/articles/324478

Neddermeyer, D.M. (2009 January 16). *Holistic Health Care Facts and Statistics.* Disabled World Holistic Health. https://www.nutraceuticalsworld.com/contents/view_breaking-news/2019-06-13/holistic-health-goals-vary-by-age/ for later use

Newlyn, E. (n.d.). *Introduction to chakras.* EkhartYoga. https://www.ekhartyoga.com/articles/practice/introduction-to-chakras

Nuts and seeds: Energy and nutrient-dense foods. (n.d.). Defeat Diabetes Foundation. https://defeatdiabetes.org/resources/healthful-eating/nuts-and-seeds/

Perfectionism and burnout: Address stress and find balance. (2018 July 7). GoodTherapy. https://www.goodtherapy.org/blog/perfectionism-burnout-address-stress-and-find-balance-0707187

Picard, C. (n.d.). *7 Signs you're dealing with anxiety, and what to do about it.* Good Housekeeping. https://www.goodhousekeeping.com/health/wellness/a27018965/anxiety-symptoms-sign-women/

Pien, G.W. (n.d.). *How does menopause affect my sleep?* Johns Hopkins Medicine. https://www.hopkinsmedicine.org/health/wellness-and-prevention/how-does-menopause-affect-my-sleep

Pietrangelo, A. (n.d.). *The effect of stress on your body.* Healthline. https://www.healthline.com/health/stress/effects-on-body

Pursed-lip Breathing. (n.d.). Cleveland Clinic. https://my.clevelandclinic.org/health/articles/9443-pursed-lip-breathing

Raman, R. (2019 March 5). *9 Health and nutrition facts of oat and bran.* Healthline. https://www.healthline.com/nutrition/oat-bran

Raypole, C. (2021 May 16). *Ready, set, journal! 64 journaling prompts for self-discovery.* PsychCentral. https://psychcentral.com/blog/ready-set-journal-64-journaling-prompts-for-self-discovery

Relaxation techniques: Breath control helps quell errant stress response. (2020 July 6). Harvard

References

Health Publishing. https://www.health.harvard.edu/mind-and-mood/relaxation-techniques-breath-control-helps-quell-errant-stress-response

Risk of sleep apnea worsens after menopause. (2000 May 11). WebMD. https://www.webmd.com/sleep-disorders/sleep-apnea/news/20000511/risk-of-sleep-apnea-worsens-after-menopause

Rhododendron (Rhododendron anthopogon) essential oil benefits. (2017 September 4). Native Essentials. https://www.nativessentials.com/blogs/clean-beauty-notes/rhododendron-essential-oil

Rogers, D.W. (2019 July 6). Breathe: *God breathes life into humanity.* Carlsbad Current Argus. https://www.currentargus.com/story/life/faith/2019/07/06/breathe-god-breathes-life-into-humanity/1660340001/

Scott, E. (2021 March 31). *Journaling to cope with anxiety.* Verywellmind. https://www.verywellmind.com/journaling-a-great-tool-for-coping-with-anxiety-3144672

Schuldt, W. (n.d.). *Therapist Aid.* https://www.therapistaid.com/therapy-article/grounding-techniques-article

Stanborough, M.F.A. (2019 December 18). *What are cognitive distortions and how can you change these thinking patterns?* Healthline. https://www.healthline.com/health/cognitive-distortions

Strauss Cohen, I. (2018 April 13). *Zen mindset: Acquiring the mindset of a master.* Psychology Today. https://www.psychologytoday.com/us/blog/your-emotional-meter/201804/zen-mindset

Suni, E. (2022 April 15). *Mental health and sleep.* Sleep Foundation. https://www.sleepfoundation.org/mental-health

Suni, E. (2022 October 7). *Stages of sleep.* Sleep Foundation. https://www.sleepfoundation.org/stages-of-sleep

The 10 best essential oils for stress in 2022. (n.d.). PsychCentral. https://psychcentral.com/health/essential-oils-for-stress

Toussaint, L., Nguyen, Q.A., Roettger, C. et al. (2021 July 2). Effectiveness of progressive muscle relaxation, deep breathing, and guided imagery in promoting psychological and physiological states of relaxation. *Pup Med Central.* https://www.ncbi.nlm.nih.gov/pmc/articles/PMC8272667/

Upham, B. (2021 November 12). *Deep breathing: A complete guide to the relaxation technique.* Everyday Health. https://www.everydayhealth.com/wellness/deep-breathing

Villines, Z. (2022 May 24). *What are chakras and how do they affect health?* MedicalNewsToday. https://www.medicalnewstoday.com/articles/what-are-chakras-concept-origins-and-effect-on-health

Voytek, B. (2013 May 20). *Brain Metrics.* Scitable [Blog] https://www.nature.com/scitable/blog/brain-metrics/are_there_really_as_many/

Wang, P., Wang, X. (2018 December). Effect of time management training on anxiety, depression, and sleep quality. *Iranian Journal of Public Health.* https://www.ncbi.nlm.nih.gov/pmc/articles/PMC6379615/

Washington, A. (2015 January 26). *The physical, mental, and emotional benefits of the warrior poses.* doyou. https://www.doyou.com/the-physical-mental-and-emotional-benefits-of-the-warrior-poses/

References

Watson, K. (n.d.). *Spirituality and stress: Is there a connection?* PsychCentral. https://psych-central.com/stress/spirituality-and-stress-relief

Watson, S. (2021 July 20). *Feel-good hormones: How they affect our mind, mood and body.* Harvard Health Publishing. https://www.health.harvard.edu/mind-and-mood/feel-good-hormones-how-they-affect-your-mind-mood-and-body

What is box breathing? (2021 April 8). WebMD.https://www.webmd.com/balance/what-is-box-breathing

Wheble, P., Manga, E. (n.d.) *What is conscious connected breathwork? Ibf* International Breathwork Foundation. https://ibfbreathwork.org/conscious-connected-breathwork/

Which basil oil is best? (2021 April 21). Amrita Aromatherapy. https://www.amri-ta.net/blog/basil-essential-oil-holy-basil-sweet-basil-tropical

Why is core strength exercise so important for seniors? (2021 November 10). The Fitness Frame. https://thefitnessframe.com/seniors-core-strength-exercise

Winston, D. (2016 February 26). *A 6-minute breathing meditation to cultivate mindfulness.* Mindful. https://www.mindful.org/a-five-minute-breathing-meditation/

Women's mental health facts. (n.d.). Agenda Alliance for Women and Girls at Risk. https://weareagenda.org/womens-mental-health-key-facts/

Wooll. M. (2022 February 2). *The secret to finding your passion isn't looking, it's doing.* BetterUp. https://www.betterup.com/blog/how-to-find-your-passion

Zen. (n.d.). Vocabulary.com. https://www.vocabulary.com/dictionary/Zen

Made in the USA
Las Vegas, NV
06 April 2024

88340240R00089